FERMAT'S
ENIGMA

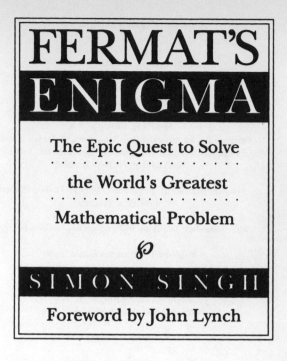

FERMAT'S ENIGMA

The Epic Quest to Solve

the World's Greatest

Mathematical Problem

SIMON SINGH

Foreword by John Lynch

Penguin Books

In memory
of
Pakhar Singh

PENGUIN BOOKS
PUBLISHED BY THE PENGUIN GROUP
Penguin Books Canada Ltd, 10 Alcorn Avenue, Toronto,
Ontario, Canada M4V 3B2
Penguin Books Ltd, 27 Wrights Lane, London W8 5TZ, England
Penguin Putnam Inc., 375 Hudson Street, New York,
New York 10014, U.S.A.
Penguin Books Australia Ltd, Ringwood, Victoria, Australia
Penguin Books (NZ) Ltd, cnr Rosedale and Airborne Roads, Albany,
Auckland 1310, New Zealand

Penguin Books Ltd, Registered Offices: Harmondsworth,
Middlesex, England

First published in Viking by Penguin Books Canada, 1997

Published in Penguin Books, 1998

1   3   5   7   9   10   8   6   4   2

Manufactured in the United States

Canadian Cataloguing in Publication Data

Singh, Simon
Fermat's enigma : the quest to solve the world's
greatest mathematical problem
ISBN 0-14-026869-3
1. Wiles, Andrew.   2. Fermat's last theorem.   I. Title.
QA244.S56   1998   512'.74   C97-930503-9

Visit Penguin Canada's web site at www.penguin.ca

Contents

. . . .

Foreword *by John Lynch*   vii
Preface   xv

1. "I Think I'll Stop Here"   1
2. The Riddler   35
3. A Mathematical Disgrace   71
4. Into Abstraction   121
5. Proof by Contradiction   171
6. The Secret Calculation   205
7. A Slight Problem   255
Epilogue: Grand Unified Mathematics   279

Appendixes   287
Suggestions for Further Reading   301
Picture Credits   306
Index   307

Foreword

· · · · · · · · ·

I finally met Andrew Wiles across a room, not crowded, but large enough to hold the entire mathematics department at Princeton. On that particular afternoon, there were not so very many people around, but enough for me to be uncertain as to which one was Wiles. After a few moments I introduced myself to the shy-looking Wiles, who had been listening to the conversation around him and sipping tea.

It was the end of an extraordinary week. I had met some of the finest mathematicians alive, and begun to gain an insight into their world. But despite every attempt to pin down Andrew Wiles, to speak to him, and to convince him to take part in a BBC *Horizon* documentary film on his achievement, this was our first meeting. This was the man who had recently announced that he had found the holy grail of mathematics; the man who claimed he had proved Fermat's Last Theorem. As we spoke, Wiles had a distracted and withdrawn air about him, and although he was polite and friendly, it was clear that he wished me as far away from him as possible. He explained very simply that he could not possibly focus on anything but his work, which was at a critical stage, but perhaps later, when the current pressures had been resolved, he would be pleased to take part. I knew, and he knew I knew, that he was facing the collapse of his life's ambition, and that the holy grail he had held was now being revealed as no more than a rather beautiful, valuable, but straightforward drinking vessel. He had found a flaw in his heralded proof.

The story of Fermat's Last Theorem is unique. By the time I first met Andrew Wiles, I had come to realize that it is truly one of the greatest stories in the sphere of scientific or academic endeavor. I had seen the headlines in the summer of 1993, when the proof had put math on the front pages of national newspapers around the world. At that time I had only a vague recollection of what the Last Theorem was, but saw that it was obviously something very special, and something that had the smell of a *Horizon* film to it. I spent the next weeks talking to many mathematicians: those closely involved in the story, or close to Andrew, and those who simply shared the thrill of witnessing a great moment in their field. All generously shared their insights into mathematical history, and patiently talked me through what little understanding I could achieve of the concepts involved. Rapidly it became clear that this was subject matter that perhaps only half a dozen people in the world could fully grasp. For a while I wondered if I was insane to attempt to make a film. But from those mathematicians I also learned of the rich history, and the deeper significance of Fermat to mathematics and its practitioners, and that, I realized, was where the real story lay.

I learned of the ancient Greek origins of the problem, and that Fermat's Last Theorem was the Himalayan peak of number theory. I was introduced to the aesthetic beauty of mathematics, and I began to appreciate what it is to describe mathematics as the language of nature. Through Wiles's contemporaries I grasped the Herculean nature of his work in pulling together all the most recent techniques of number theory to apply to his proof. From his friends at Princeton I heard of the intricate progress of Andrew's years of isolated study. I built up an extraordinary picture around Andrew Wiles, and the puzzle that dominated his life.

Although the math involved in Wiles's proof is some of the toughest in the world, I found that the beauty of Fermat's Last Theorem lies in the fact that the problem itself is supremely simple to understand. It is a puzzle that is stated in terms familiar to every schoolchild. Pierre de Fermat was a man in the Renaissance tradition, who was at the center of the rediscovery of ancient Greek knowledge, but he asked a question that the Greeks would not have thought to ask, and in so doing produced what became the hardest problem on earth for others to solve. Tantalizingly, he left a note for posterity suggesting that he had an answer, but not what it was. That was the beginning of the chase that lasted three centuries.

That time span underlies the significance of this puzzle. It is hard to conceive of any problem, in any discipline of science, so simply and clearly stated that could have withstood the test of advancing knowledge for so long. Consider the leaps in understanding in physics, chemistry, biology, medicine, and engineering that have occurred since the seventeenth century. We have progressed from "humors" in medicine to gene-splicing, we have identified the fundamental atomic particles, and we have placed men on the moon, but in number theory Fermat's Last Theorem remained inviolate.

For some time in my research I looked for a reason why the Last Theorem mattered to anyone but a mathematician, and why it would be important to make a program about it. Mathematics has a multitude of practical applications, but in the case of number theory the most exciting uses that I was offered were in cryptography, in the design of acoustic baffling, and in communication from distant spacecraft. None of these seemed likely to draw in an audience. What was far more compelling were the mathematicians themselves, and the sense of passion that they all expressed when talking of Fermat.

Mathematics is one of the purest forms of thought, and to outsiders mathematicians may seem almost otherworldly. The thing that struck me in all my discussions with them was the extraordinary precision of their conversation. A question was rarely answered immediately. Instead, I would often have to wait while the precise structure of the answer was resolved in the mind, but it would then emerge, as articulate and careful a statement as I could have wished for. When I tackled Andrew's friend Peter Sarnak on this, he explained that mathematicians simply hate to make a false statement. Of course they use intuition and inspiration, but formal statements have to be absolute. Proof is what lies at the heart of math, and is what marks it out from other sciences. Other sciences have hypotheses that are tested against experimental evidence until they fail, and are overtaken by new hypotheses. In math, absolute proof is the goal, and once something is proved, it is proved forever, with no room for change. In the Last Theorem, mathematicians had their greatest challenge of proof, and the person who found the answer would receive the adulation of the entire discipline.

Prizes were offered, and rivalry flourished. The Last Theorem has a rich history that touches death and deception, and it has even spurred on the development of mathematics. As the Harvard mathematician Barry Mazur has put it, Fermat added a certain "animus" to those areas of mathematics that were associated with early attempts at the proof. Ironically, it turned out that just such an area of math was central to Wiles's final proof.

Gradually picking up an understanding of this unfamiliar field, I came to appreciate Fermat's Last Theorem as central to, and even a parallel for, the development of mathematics itself.

Fermat was the father of modern number theory, and since his time mathematics had evolved, progressed, and diversified into many arcane areas, where new techniques had spawned new areas of mathematics, and become ends in themselves. As the centuries passed, the Last Theorem came to seem less and less relevant to the cutting edge of mathematical research, and more and more turned into a curiosity. But it is now clear that its centrality to math never diminished.

Problems around numbers, such as the one Fermat posed, are like playground puzzles, and mathematicians like solving puzzles. To Andrew Wiles it was a very special puzzle, and nothing less than his life's ambition. When he first revealed a proof in that summer of 1993, it came at the end of seven years of dedicated work on the problem, a degree of focus and determination that is hard to imagine. Many of the techniques he used had not been created when he began. He also drew together the work of many fine mathematicians, linking ideas and creating concepts that others had feared to attempt. In a sense, reflected Barry Mazur, it turned out that everyone had been working on Fermat, but separately and without having it as a goal, for the proof had required all the power of modern mathematics to be brought to bear upon its solution. What Andrew had done was tie together once again areas of mathematics that had seemed far apart. His work therefore seemed to be a justification of all the diversification that mathematics had undergone since the problem had been stated.

At the heart of his proof of Fermat, Andrew had proved an idea known as the Taniyama-Shimura conjecture, which created a new bridge between wildly different mathematical worlds. For many, the goal of one unified mathematics is supreme, and this was a glimpse of just such a world. So in proving Fermat, Andrew Wiles had cemented some of the most important number theory of the postwar period and had secured the base of a pyramid of conjectures that were built upon it. This was no longer simply solving the longest-standing mathematical puzzle, but was pushing the very boundaries of mathematics itself. It was as if Fermat's simple problem, born at a time when math was in its infancy, had been waiting for this moment.

For mathematicians, the level of emotion was intense. All were reveling in the glorious moment.

With all this in train, small wonder at the weight of responsibility that Wiles felt as the flaw had gradually emerged over the autumn of 1993. With the eyes of the world upon him, and his colleagues calling to have the proof made public, somehow, and only he knows how, he didn't crack. He had moved from doing math in privacy and at his own pace to suddenly working in public. Andrew is an intensely private man, who fought hard to keep his family sheltered from the storm that was breaking around him. Throughout that week while I was in Princeton, I called, I left notes at his office, on his doorstep, and with his friends; I even provided a gift of English tea. But he resisted my overtures, until that chance meeting on the day of my departure. A quiet, intense conversation followed, which in the end lasted barely fifteen minutes.

When we parted that afternoon there was an understanding between us. If he managed to repair the proof, then he would come to me to discuss a film; I was prepared to wait. But as I flew home to London that night it seemed to me that the television program was dead. No one had ever repaired a hole in the many attempted proofs of Fermat in three centuries. History was littered with false claims, and much as I wished that he would be the exception, it was hard to imagine Wiles as anything but another headstone in that mathematical graveyard.

A year later I received the call. After an extraordinary mathematical twist, and a flash of true insight and inspiration, Wiles had finally brought an end to Fermat. The following year we found the time for him to devote to filming. By this time I had invited Simon Singh to join me in making the film, and together we spent time with Andrew, learning from the man himself the full story of those seven years of isolated study, and his year of hell that followed. As we filmed, Andrew told us, as he had told no one before, of his innermost feelings about what he had done; how for thirty years he had hung on to a childhood dream; how so much of the math he had ever studied had been, without his really knowing it at the time, really a gathering of tools for the Fermat challenge that had dominated his career; how nothing would ever be the same; of his sense of loss for the problem that would no longer be his constant companion; and of the uplifting sense of release that he now felt. For a field in which the subject matter is technically about as difficult for a lay audience to understand as can be imagined, the level of emotional charge in our conversations was greater than any I have experienced in a career in science film making. For Andrew Wiles it was the end of a chapter in his life. For me it was a privilege to be close to it.

The film, *Fermat's Last Theorem*, was transmitted in Britain on BBC Television as part of the *Horizon* series, and then in the United States on PBS's *Nova* series. Simon Singh has now developed those insights and intimate conversations, together with the full richness of the Fermat story and the history and mathematics that have always hung around it, into this book, which is a complete and enlightening record of one of the greatest stories in human thinking.

John Lynch
Editor of BBC TV's *Horizon* series
March 1997

Preface
. . . .

The story of Fermat's Last Theorem is inextricably linked with the history of mathematics, touching on all the major themes of number theory. It provides a unique insight into what drives mathematics and, perhaps more important, what inspires mathematicians. The Last Theorem is at the heart of an intriguing saga of courage, skulduggery, cunning, and tragedy, involving all the greatest heroes of mathematics.

Fermat's Last Theorem has its origins in the mathematics of ancient Greece, two thousand years before Pierre de Fermat constructed the problem in the form we know it today. Hence, it links the foundations of mathematics created by Pythagoras to the most sophisticated ideas in modern mathematics. In writing this book I have chosen a largely chronological structure that begins by describing the revolutionary ethos of the Pythagorean Brotherhood, and ends with Andrew Wiles's personal story of his struggle to find a solution to Fermat's conundrum.

Chapter 1 tells the story of Pythagoras, and describes how Pythagoras's theorem is the direct ancestor of the Last Theorem. This chapter also discusses some of the fundamental concepts of mathematics that will recur throughout the book. Chapter 2 takes the story from ancient Greece to seventeenth-century France, where Pierre de Fermat created the most profound riddle in the history of mathematics. Fermat was an extraordinary character whose contribution to mathematics goes far beyond the Last Theorem. I have spent several pages describing his life and some of his other brilliant discoveries.

Chapters 3 and 4 describe some of the attempts to prove Fermat's Last Theorem during the eighteenth, nineteenth, and early twentieth centuries. Although these efforts ended in failure they led to a marvelous arsenal of mathematical techniques and tools, some of which have been integral to the very latest attempts to prove the Last Theorem. In addition to describing the mathematics, I have devoted much of these chapters to the mathematicians who became obsessed by Fermat's legacy. Their stories show how mathematicians were prepared to sacrifice everything in the search for truth, and how mathematics has evolved through the centuries.

The remaining chapters of the book chronicle the remarkable events of the last forty years that have revolutionized the study of Fermat's Last Theorem. In particular, Chapters 6 and 7 focus on the work of Andrew Wiles, whose breakthroughs in the last decade astonished the mathematical community. These later chapters are based on extensive interviews with Wiles. This was a unique opportunity for me to hear at first hand one of the most extraordinary intellectual journeys of the twentieth century, and I hope that I have been able to convey the creativity and heroism that was required during Wiles's ten-year ordeal.

In telling the tale of Pierre de Fermat and his baffling riddle I have tried to describe the mathematical concepts without resorting to equations, but inevitably x, y, and z do occasionally rear their ugly heads. When equations do appear in the text I have endeavored to provide sufficient explanation such that even readers with no background in mathematics will be able to understand their significance. For those readers with a slightly deeper knowledge of the subject I have provided a series of appendices that expand on the mathematical ideas contained in the main text. In addition, I have included a list of further reading, which is generally aimed at providing the layperson with more detail about particular areas of mathematics.

This book would not have been possible without the help and involvement of many people. In particular I would like to thank Andrew Wiles, who went out of his way to give long and detailed interviews during a time of intense pressure. During my seven years as a science journalist I have never met anybody with a greater level of passion and commitment to their subject, and I am eternally grateful that Professor Wiles was prepared to share his story with me.

I would also like to thank the other mathematicians who helped me in the writing of this book and who allowed me to interview them at length. Some of them have been deeply involved in tackling Fermat's Last Theorem, while others were witnesses to the historic events of the last forty years. The hours I spent quizzing and chatting with them were enormously enjoyable, and I appreciate their patience and enthusiasm while explaining so many beautiful mathematical concepts to me. In particular I would like to thank John Coates, John Conway, Nick Katz, Barry Mazur, Ken Ribet, Peter Sarnak, Goro Shimura, and Richard Taylor.

I have tried to illustrate this book with as many portraits as possible to give the reader a better sense of the characters involved in the story of Fermat's Last Theorem. Various libraries and archives have gone out of their way to help me, and in particular I would like to thank Susan Oakes of the London Mathematical Society, Sandra Cumming of the Royal Society, and Ian Stewart of Warwick University. I am also grateful to Jacquelyn Savani of Princeton University, Duncan McAngus, Jeremy Gray, Paul

Balister, and the Isaac Newton Institute for their help in finding research material. Thanks also go to Dawn Dzedzy, Patrick Walsh, Christopher Potter, Bernadette Alves, Sanjida O'Connell, and my parents for their comments and support throughout the last year.

Finally, many of the interviews quoted in this book were obtained while I was working on a television documentary on the subject of Fermat's Last Theorem. I would like to thank the BBC for allowing me to use this material, and in particular I owe a debt of gratitude to John Lynch, who worked with me on the documentary, and who helped to inspire my interest in the subject.

Although Fermat's Last Theorem has been the world's hardest mathematical problem, I hope that I have succeeded in conveying an understanding of the mathematics involved in tackling it, and an insight into why mathematicians have been obsessed by it for more than three centuries. Mathematics is one of the purest and most profound of intellectual disciplines, and my intention has been to provide readers a glimpse into this fascinating world.

FERMAT'S
ENIGMA

Andrew Wiles aged ten years, when he first encountered Fermat's Last Theorem.

1

"I Think I'll Stop Here"

. . . .

Archimedes will be remembered when Aeschylus is forgotten, because languages die and mathematical ideas do not. "Immortality" may be a silly word, but probably a mathematician has the best chance of whatever it may mean.

G. H. Hardy

June 23, 1993, Cambridge

It was the most important mathematics lecture of the century. Two hundred mathematicians were transfixed. Only a quarter of them fully understood the dense mixture of Greek symbols and algebra that covered the blackboard. The rest were there merely to witness what they hoped would be a truly historic occasion.

The rumors had started the previous day. Electronic mail over the Internet had hinted that the lecture would culminate in a solution to Fermat's Last Theorem, the world's most famous mathematical problem. Such gossip was not uncommon. The subject of the Last Theorem would often crop up over tea, and mathematicians would speculate as to who might be doing what. Sometimes mathematical mutterings in the senior common room would turn the speculation into rumors of a breakthrough, but nothing had ever materialized.

This time the rumor was different. When the three black-

1

boards became full, the lecturer paused. The first board was erased and the algebra continued. Each line of mathematics appeared to be one tiny step closer to the solution, but after thirty minutes the lecturer had still not announced the proof. The professors crammed into the front rows waited eagerly for the conclusion. The students standing at the back looked to their seniors for hints of what the conclusion might be. Were they watching a complete proof to Fermat's Last Theorem, or was the lecturer merely outlining an incomplete and anticlimactic argument?

The lecturer was Andrew Wiles, a reserved Englishman who had emigrated to America in the 1980s and taken up a professorship at Princeton University, where he had earned a reputation as one of the most talented mathematicians of his generation. However, in recent years he had almost vanished from the annual round of conferences and seminars, and colleagues had begun to assume that Wiles was finished. It is not unusual for brilliant young minds to burn out, a point noted by the mathematician Alfred Adler: "The mathematical life of a mathematician is short. Work rarely improves after the age of twenty-five or thirty. If little has been accomplished by then, little will ever be accomplished."

"Young men should prove theorems, old men should write books," observed G. H. Hardy in his book *A Mathematician's Apology*. "No mathematician should ever forget that mathematics, more than any other art or science, is a young man's game. To take a simple illustration, the average age of election to the Royal Society is lowest in mathematics." His own most brilliant student, Srinivasa Ramanujan, was elected a Fellow of the Royal Society at the age of just thirty-one, having made a series of outstanding breakthroughs during his youth. Despite having received very little formal education in his home village of

Kumbakonam in South India, Ramanujan was able to create theorems and solutions that had evaded mathematicians in the West. In mathematics the experience that comes with age seems less important than the intuition and daring of youth.

Many mathematicians have had brilliant but short careers. The nineteenth-century Norwegian Niels Henrik Abel made his greatest contribution to mathematics at the age of nineteen and died in poverty, just eight years later, of tuberculosis. Charles Hermite said of him, "He has left mathematicians something to keep them busy for five hundred years," and it is certainly true that Abel's discoveries still have a profound influence on today's number theorists. Abel's equally gifted contemporary Évariste Galois also made his breakthroughs while still a teenager.

Hardy once said, "I do not know an instance of a major mathematical advance initiated by a man past fifty." Middle-aged mathematicians often fade into the background and occupy their remaining years teaching or administrating rather than researching. In the case of Andrew Wiles nothing could be further from the truth. Although he had reached the grand old age of forty he had spent the last seven years working in complete secrecy, attempting to solve the single greatest problem in mathematics. While others suspected he had dried up, Wiles was making fantastic progress, inventing new techniques and tools that he was now ready to reveal. His decision to work in absolute isolation was a high-risk strategy and one that was unheard of in the world of mathematics.

Without inventions to patent, the mathematics department of any university is the least secretive of all. The community prides itself in an open and free exchange of ideas and afternoon breaks have evolved into daily rituals during which concepts are shared and explored over tea or coffee. As a result it is increasingly common to find papers being published by coauthors or teams of mathematicians, and consequently the glory is shared out equally. However, if Professor Wiles had genuinely discovered a complete and accurate proof of Fermat's Last Theorem, then the most wanted prize in mathematics was his and his alone. The price he had to pay for his secrecy was that since he had not previously discussed or tested any of his ideas with the mathematics community, there was a significant chance that he had made some fundamental error.

Ideally Wiles had wanted to spend more time going over his work and checking fully his final manuscript. But when the unique opportunity arose to announce his discovery at the Isaac Newton Institute in Cambridge he abandoned caution. The sole aim of the institute's existence is to bring together the world's greatest intellects for a few weeks in order to hold seminars on a cutting-edge research topic of their choice. Situated on the outskirts of the university, away from students and other distractions, the building is especially designed to encourage the academics to concentrate on collaboration and brainstorming. There are no dead-end corridors in which to hide and every office faces a central forum. The mathematicians are supposed to spend time in this open area, and are discouraged from keeping their office doors closed. Collaboration while moving around the institute is also encouraged — even the elevator, which travels only three floors, contains a blackboard. In fact every room in the building has at least one blackboard, including the bathrooms. On this occasion the seminars at the Newton Institute came under the heading of "*L*-functions and Arithmetic." All the world's top number theorists had been gathered together in order to discuss problems relating to this highly specialized area of pure mathematics, but only Wiles realized that *L*-functions might hold the key to solving Fermat's Last Theorem.

Although he had been attracted by having the opportunity to reveal his work to such an eminent audience, the main reason for making the announcement at the Newton Institute was that it was in his hometown, Cambridge. This was where Wiles had been born, it was here he grew up and developed his passion for numbers, and it was in Cambridge that he had alighted on the problem that was to dominate the rest of his life.

The Last Problem

In 1963, when he was ten years old, Andrew Wiles was already fascinated by mathematics. "I loved doing the problems in school. I'd take them home and make up new ones of my own. But the best problem I ever found I discovered in my local library."

One day, while wandering home from school, young Wiles decided to visit the library in Milton Road. It was rather small, but it had a generous collection of puzzle books, and this is what often caught Andrew's attention. These books were packed with all sorts of scientific conundrums and mathematical riddles, and for each question the solution would be conveniently laid out somewhere in the final few pages. But this time Andrew was drawn to a book with only one problem, and no solution.

The book was *The Last Problem* by Eric Temple Bell. It gave the history of a mathematical problem that has its roots in ancient Greece, but that reached full maturity only in the seventeenth century when the French mathematician Pierre de Fermat inadvertently set it as a challenge for the rest of the world. One great mathematician after another had been humbled by Fermat's legacy, and for three hundred years nobody had been able to solve it.

Thirty years after first reading Bell's account, Wiles could remember how he felt the moment he was introduced to Fermat's Last Theorem: "It looked so simple, and yet all the great mathematicians in history couldn't solve it. Here was a problem that I, a ten-year-old, could understand and I knew from that moment that I would never let it go. I had to solve it."

Usually half the difficulty in a mathematics problem is understanding the question, but in this case it was straightforward — prove that there are no whole number solutions for this equation:

$$x^n + y^n = z^n \text{ for } n \text{ greater than 2.}$$

The problem has a simple and familiar look to it because it is based on the one piece of mathematics that everyone can remember — Pythagoras's theorem:

> In a right-angled triangle the square on the hypotenuse is
> equal to the sum of the squares on the other two sides.

$$\text{Or: } x^2 + y^2 = z^2.$$

Pythagoras's theorem has been scorched into millions if not billions of human brains. It is the fundamental theorem that every innocent schoolchild is forced to learn. But despite the fact that it can be understood by a ten-year-old, Pythagoras's creation was the inspiration for a problem that had thwarted the greatest mathematical minds of history.

In the sixth century B.C., Pythagoras of Samos was one of the most influential and yet mysterious figures in mathematics. Because there are no firsthand accounts of his life and work, he is shrouded in myth and legend, making it difficult for historians to separate fact from fiction. What seems certain is that Pythagoras developed the idea of numerical logic and was responsible for the first golden age of mathematics. Thanks to his genius numbers were no longer merely used to count and calculate, but were appreciated in their own right. He studied the properties of particular numbers, the relationships between them, and the patterns they formed. He realized that numbers exist independently of the tangible world and therefore their study was untainted by the inaccuracies of perception. This meant he could discover truths that were independent of opinion or prejudice and that were more absolute than any previous knowledge.

He gained his mathematical skills on his travels throughout the ancient world. Some tales would have us believe that Pythagoras traveled as far as India and Britain, but what is more certain is that he gathered many mathematical techniques from the Egyptians and Babylonians. Both these ancient peoples had gone beyond the limits of simple counting and were capable of performing complex calculations that enabled them to create sophisticated accounting systems and construct elaborate buildings. Indeed they saw mathematics as merely a tool for solving practical problems; the motivation behind discovering some of the basic rules of geometry was to allow reconstruction of field boundaries that were lost in the annual flooding of the Nile. The word itself, geometry, means "to measure the earth."

Pythagoras observed that the Egyptians and Babylonians conducted each calculation in the form of a recipe that could be followed blindly. The recipes, which would have been passed down through the generations, always gave the correct answer and so nobody bothered to question them or explore the logic underlying the equations. What was important for these civilizations was that a calculation worked — why it worked was irrelevant.

After twenty years of travel Pythagoras had assimilated all the mathematical rules in the known world. He set sail for his home island of Samos in the Aegean Sea with the intention of founding a school devoted to the study of philosophy and, in particular, concerned with research into his newly acquired mathematical rules. He wanted to understand numbers, not merely exploit them. He hoped to find a plentiful supply of free-thinking students who could help him develop radical new philosophies, but during his absence the tyrant Polycrates had turned the once liberal Samos into an intolerant and conservative society. Polycrates invited Pythagoras to join his court, but the philosopher realized that this was only a maneuver aimed at silencing him and therefore declined the honor. Instead he left the city in favor of a cave in a remote part of the island, where he could contemplate without fear of persecution.

Pythagoras did not relish his isolation and eventually resorted to bribing a young boy to be his first pupil. The identity of the boy is uncertain, but some historians have suggested that his name was also Pythagoras, and that the student would later gain fame as the first person to suggest that athletes should eat meat to improve their physiques. Pythagoras, the teacher, paid his student three oboli for each lesson he attended and noticed that as the weeks passed the boy's initial reluctance to learn was transformed into an enthusiasm for knowledge. To test his pupil Pythagoras pretended that he could no longer afford to pay the student and that the lessons would have to stop, at which point the boy offered to pay for his education rather than have it ended. The pupil had become a disciple. Unfortunately this was Pythagoras's only conversion on Samos. He did temporarily establish a school, known as the Semicircle of Pythagoras, but his views on social reform were unacceptable and the philosopher was forced to flee the colony with his mother and his one and only disciple.

Pythagoras departed for southern Italy, which was then a part of Magna Graecia, and settled in Croton, where he was fortunate in finding the ideal patron in Milo, the wealthiest man in Croton and one of the strongest men in history. Although Pythagoras's reputation as the sage of Samos was already spreading across Greece, Milo's fame was even greater. Milo was a man of Herculean proportions who had been champion of the Olympic and Pythian Games a record twelve times. In addition to his athleticism Milo also appreciated and studied philosophy and mathematics. He set aside part of his house and provided Pythagoras with enough room to establish a school. So it was that the most creative mind and the most powerful body formed a partnership.

Secure in his new home, Pythagoras founded the Pythagorean Brotherhood — a band of six hundred followers who were capable not only of understanding his teachings, but who could add to them by creating new ideas and proofs. Upon entering the Brotherhood each follower had to donate all his worldly possessions to a common fund, and should anybody ever leave he would receive twice the amount he had originally donated and a tombstone would be erected in his memory. The Brotherhood was an egalitarian school and included several sisters. Pythagoras's favorite student was Milo's own daughter, the beautiful Theano, and, despite the difference in their ages, they eventually married.

Soon after founding the Brotherhood, Pythagoras coined the word *philosopher*, and in so doing defined the aims of his school. While attending the Olympic Games, Leon, Prince of Phlius, asked Pythagoras how he would describe himself. Pythagoras replied, "I am a philosopher," but Leon had not heard the word before and asked him to explain.

Life, Prince Leon, may well be compared with these public Games for in the vast crowd assembled here some are attracted by the acquisition of gain, others are led on by the hopes and ambitions of fame and glory. But among them there are a few who have come to observe and to understand all that passes here.

It is the same with life. Some are influenced by the love of wealth while others are blindly led on by the mad fever for power and domination, but the finest type of man gives himself up to discovering the meaning and purpose of life itself. He seeks to uncover the secrets of nature. This is the man I call a philosopher for although no man is completely wise in all respects, he can love wisdom as the key to nature's secrets.

Although many were aware of Pythagoras's aspirations, nobody outside of the Brotherhood knew the details or extent of his success. Each member of the school was forced to swear an oath never to reveal to the outside world any of their mathematical discoveries. Even after Pythagoras's death a member of the Brotherhood was drowned for breaking his oath — he publicly announced the discovery of a new regular solid, the dodecahedron, constructed from twelve regular pentagons. The highly secretive nature of the Pythagorean Brotherhood is part of the reason that myths have developed surrounding the strange rituals that they might have practiced, and similarly this is why there are so few reliable accounts of their mathematical achievements.

What is known for certain is that Pythagoras established an ethos that changed the course of mathematics. The Brotherhood was effectively a religious community, and one of the idols they worshiped was Number. By understanding the relationships between numbers, they believed that they could uncover the spiritual secrets of the universe and bring themselves closer to the gods. In particular the Brotherhood focused its attention on the study of counting numbers (1, 2, 3, ...) and fractions. Counting numbers are sometimes called *whole numbers*, and, together with fractions (ratios between whole numbers), they are technically referred to as *rational numbers*. Among the infinity of numbers, the Brotherhood looked for those with special significance, and some of the most special were the so-called "perfect" numbers.

According to Pythagoras, numerical perfection depended on a number's divisors (numbers that will divide perfectly into the original one). For instance, the divisors of 12 are 1, 2, 3, 4, and 6. When the sum of a number's divisors is greater than the number itself, it is called an "excessive" number. Therefore 12 is an excessive number because its divisors add up to 16. On the other hand, when the sum of a number's divisors is less than the number itself, it is called "defective." So 10 is a defective number because its divisors (1, 2, and 5) add up to only 8.

The most significant and rarest numbers are those whose divisors add up exactly to the number itself, and these are the *perfect numbers*. The number 6 has the divisors 1, 2, and 3, and consequently it is a perfect number because $1 + 2 + 3 = 6$. The next perfect number is 28, because $1 + 2 + 4 + 7 + 14 = 28$.

As well as having mathematical significance for the Brotherhood, the perfection of 6 and 28 was acknowledged by other cultures who observed that the moon orbits the earth every 28 days and who declared that God created the world in 6 days. In *The City of God,* St. Augustine argues that although God could have created the world in an instant he decided to take six days in order to reflect the universe's perfection. St. Augustine observed that 6 was not perfect because God chose it, but rather that the perfection was inherent in the nature of the number: "6 is a number perfect in itself, and not because God created all things in six days; rather the inverse is true; God created all things in six days because this number is perfect. And it would remain perfect even if the work of the six days did not exist."

As the counting numbers get bigger the perfect numbers become harder to find. The third perfect number is 496, the fourth is 8,128, the fifth is 33,550,336, and the sixth is 8,589,869,056. As well as being the sum of their divisors, Pythagoras noted that all perfect numbers exhibit several other elegant properties. For example, perfect numbers are always the sum of a series of consecutive counting numbers. So we have

$$6 = 1 + 2 + 3,$$
$$28 = 1 + 2 + 3 + 4 + 5 + 6 + 7,$$
$$496 = 1 + 2 + 3 + 4 + 5 + 6 + 7 + 8 + 9 + \cdots + 30 + 31,$$
$$8,128 = 1 + 2 + 3 + 4 + 5 + 6 + 7 + 8 + 9 + \cdots + 126 + 127.$$

Pythagoras was entertained by perfect numbers, but he was not satisfied with merely collecting these special numbers; instead he desired to discover their deeper significance. One of his insights was that perfection was closely linked to "twoness." The numbers 4 (2×2), 8 $(2 \times 2 \times 2)$, 16 $(2 \times 2 \times 2 \times 2)$, etc., are known as powers of 2, and can be written as 2^n, where the n represents the number of 2's multiplied together. All these powers of 2 only just fail to be perfect, because the sum of their divisors always adds up to one less than the number itself. This makes them only slightly defective:

$2^2 = 2 \times 2$	= **4**,	Divisors 1, 2	Sum = **3**,
$2^3 = 2 \times 2 \times 2$	= **8**,	Divisors 1, 2, 4	Sum = **7**,
$2^4 = 2 \times 2 \times 2 \times 2$	= **16**,	Divisors 1, 2, 4, 8	Sum = **15**,
$2^5 = 2 \times 2 \times 2 \times 2 \times 2$	= **32**,	Divisors 1, 2, 4, 8, 16	Sum = **31**.

Two centuries later Euclid would refine Pythagoras's link between twoness and perfection. Euclid discovered that perfect numbers are always the multiple of two numbers, one of which is a power of 2 and the other being the next power of 2 minus 1. That is to say,

$$6 = 2^1 \times (2^2 - 1),$$
$$28 = 2^2 \times (2^3 - 1),$$
$$496 = 2^4 \times (2^5 - 1),$$
$$8,128 = 2^6 \times (2^7 - 1).$$

Today's computers have continued the search for perfect numbers and find such enormously large examples as $2^{216,090} \times (2^{216,091}-1)$, a number with over 130,000 digits, which obeys Euclid's rule.

Pythagoras was fascinated by the rich patterns and properties possessed by perfect numbers and respected their subtlety and cunning. At first sight perfection is a relatively simple concept to grasp, and yet the ancient Greeks were unable to fathom some of the fundamental points of the subject. For example, although there are plenty of numbers whose divisors add up to one less than the number itself, that is to say only slightly defective, there appear to be no numbers that are slightly excessive. The Greeks were unable to find any numbers whose divisors added up to one more than the number itself, but they could not explain why this was the case. Frustratingly, although they failed to discover slightly excessive numbers, they could not prove that no such numbers existed. Understanding the apparent lack of slightly excessive numbers was of no practical value whatsoever; nonetheless it was a problem that might illuminate the nature of numbers and therefore it was worthy of study. Such riddles intrigued the Pythagorean Brotherhood, and two and a half thousand years later, mathematicians are still unable to prove that no slightly excessive numbers exist.

Everything Is Number

In addition to studying the relationships within numbers, Pythagoras was also intrigued by the link between numbers and nature. He realized that natural phenomena are governed by laws, and that these laws could be described by mathematical equations. One of the first links he discovered was the fundamental relationship between the harmony of music and the harmony of numbers.

The most important instrument in early Hellenic music was the tetrachord, or four-stringed lyre. Prior to Pythagoras, musicians appreciated that particular notes when sounded together created a pleasant effect, and tuned their lyres so that plucking two strings would generate such a harmony. However, the early musicians had no understanding of why particular notes were harmonious and had no objective system for tuning their instruments. Instead they tuned their lyres purely by ear until a state of harmony was established — a process that Plato called torturing the tuning pegs.

Iamblichus, the fourth-century scholar who wrote nine books about the Pythagorean sect, describes how Pythagoras came to discover the underlying principles of musical harmony:

> Once he was engrossed in the thought of whether he could devise a mechanical aid for the sense of hearing which would prove both certain and ingenious. Such an aid would be similar to the compasses, rules and optical instruments designed for the sense of sight. Likewise the sense of touch had scales and the concepts of weights and measures. By some divine stroke of luck he happened to walk past the forge of a blacksmith and listened to the hammers pounding iron and producing a variegated harmony of reverberations between them, except for one combination of sounds.

According to Iamblichus, Pythagoras immediately ran into the forge to investigate the harmony of the hammers. He noticed that most of the hammers could be struck simultaneously to generate a harmonious sound, whereas any combination containing one particular hammer always generated an unpleasant noise. He analyzed the hammers and realized that those that were harmonious with each other had a simple mathematical relationship — their masses were simple ratios or fractions of each other. That is to say that hammers half, two-thirds, or three-quarters the weight of a particular hammer would all generate harmonious sounds. On the other hand, the hammer that was generating disharmony when struck along with any of the other hammers had a weight that bore no simple relationship to the other weights.

Pythagoras had discovered that simple numerical ratios were responsible for harmony in music. Scientists have cast some doubt on Iamblichus's account of this story, but what is more certain is how Pythagoras applied his new theory of musical ratios to the lyre by examining the properties of a single string. Simply plucking the string generates a standard note or tone that is produced by the entire length of the vibrating string. By fixing the string at particular points along its length, it is possible to generate other vibrations and tones, as illustrated in Figure 1. Crucially, harmonious tones occur only at very specific points. For example, by fixing the string at a point exactly halfway along it, plucking generates a tone that is one octave higher and in harmony with the original tone. Similarly, by fixing the string at points that are exactly a third, a quarter, or a fifth of the way along it, other harmonious notes are produced. However, by fixing the string at a point that is not a simple fraction along the length of the whole string, a tone is generated that is not in harmony with the other tones.

Figure 1. A freely vibrating open string generates a ground note. By creating a node exactly halfway along the string, the note generated is one octave higher and in harmony with the original note. Other harmonic notes can be generated by moving the node to other positions that are simple fractions (e.g., a third, a quarter, a fifth) of the distance along the string.

Pythagoras had uncovered for the first time the mathematical rule that governs a physical phenomenon and demonstrated that there was a fundamental relationship between mathematics and science. Ever since this discovery scientists have searched for the mathematical rules that appear to govern every single physical process and have found that numbers crop up in all manner of natural phenomena. For example, one particular number appears to guide the lengths of meandering rivers. Professor Hans-Henrik Stølum, an earth scientist at Cambridge University, has calculated the ratio between the actual length of rivers from source to mouth and their direct length as the crow flies. Although the ratio varies from river to river, the average value is slightly greater than 3, that is to say that the actual length is roughly three times greater than the direct distance. In fact the ratio is approximately 3.14, which is close to the value of the number π, the ratio between the circumference of a circle and its diameter.

The number π was originally derived from the geometry of circles, and yet it reappears over and over again in a variety of scientific circumstances. In the case of the river ratio, the appearance of π is the result of a battle between order and chaos. Einstein was the first to suggest that rivers have a tendency toward an ever more loopy path because the slightest curve will lead to faster currents on the outer side, which will in turn result in more erosion and a sharper bend. The sharper the bend, the faster the currents on the outer edge, the more the erosion, the more the river will twist, and so on. However, there is a natural process that will curtail the chaos: increasing loopiness will result in rivers doubling back on themselves and effectively short-circuiting. The river will become straighter and the loop will be left to one side, forming an oxbow lake. The balance between these two opposing factors leads to an average ratio of π between the actual length and the direct distance between source and mouth. The ratio of π is most commonly found for rivers flowing across very gently sloping plains, such as those found in Brazil or the Siberian tundra.

Pythagoras realized that numbers were hidden in everything, from the harmonies of music to the orbits of planets, and this led him to proclaim that "Everything Is Number." By exploring the meaning of mathematics, Pythagoras was developing the language that would enable him and others to describe the nature of the universe. Henceforth each breakthrough in mathematics would give scientists the vocabulary they needed to better explain the phenomena around them. In fact developments in mathematics would inspire revolutions in science.

Of all the links between numbers and nature studied by the Brotherhood, the most important was the relationship that bears their founder's name. Pythagoras's theorem provides us with an equation that is true of all right-angled triangles and that therefore also defines the right angle itself. In turn, the right angle defines the perpendicular and the perpendicular defines the dimensions—length, width, and height—of the space in which we live. Ultimately mathematics, via the right-angled triangle, defines the very structure of our three-dimensional world.

It is a profound realization, and yet the mathematics required to grasp Pythagoras's theorem is relatively simple. To understand it, simply begin by measuring the length of the two short sides of a right-angled triangle (x and y), and then square each one (x^2, y^2). Then add the two squared numbers ($x^2 + y^2$) to give you a final number. If you work out this number for the triangle shown in Figure 2, then the answer is 25.

You can now measure the longest side z, the so-called hypotenuse, and square this length. The remarkable result is that this number z^2 is identical to the one you just calculated, i.e., $5^2 = 25$.

$$x = 3, \ y = 4, \ z = 5$$
$$x^2 + y^2 = z^2$$
$$9 + 16 = 25$$

Figure 2. All right-angled triangles obey Pythagoras's theorem.

That is to say,

> In a right-angled triangle the square on the hypotenuse is equal to the sum of the squares on the other two sides.

Or in other words (or rather symbols):

$$x^2 + y^2 = z^2.$$

This is clearly true for the triangle in Figure 2, but what is remarkable is that Pythagoras's theorem is true for every right-angled triangle you can possibly imagine. It is a universal law of mathematics, and you can rely on it whenever you come across any triangle with a right angle. Conversely if you have a triangle that obeys Pythagoras's theorem, then you can be absolutely confident that it is a right-angled triangle.

At this point it is important to note that, although this theorem will forever be associated with Pythagoras, it was actually used by the Chinese and the Babylonians one thousand years before. However, these cultures did not know that the theorem was true for every right-angled triangle. It was certainly true for the triangles they tested, but they had no way of showing that it was true for all the right-angled triangles that they had not tested. The reason for Pythagoras's claim to the theorem is that it was he who first demonstrated its universal truth.

But how did Pythagoras know that his theorem is true for every right-angled triangle? He could not hope to test the infinite variety of right-angled triangles, and yet he could still be one hundred percent sure of the theorem's absolute truth. The reason for his confidence lies in the concept of mathematical proof. The search for a mathematical proof is the search for a knowledge that is more absolute than the knowledge accumulated by any other discipline. The desire for ultimate truth via the method of proof is what has driven mathematicians for the last two and a half thousand years.

Absolute Proof

The story of Fermat's Last Theorem revolves around the search for a missing proof. Mathematical proof is far more powerful and rigorous than the concept of proof we casually use in our everyday language, or even the concept of proof as understood by physicists or chemists. The difference between scientific and mathematical proof is both subtle and profound, and is crucial to understanding the work of every mathematician since Pythagoras.

The idea of a classic mathematical proof is to begin with a series of axioms, statements that can be assumed to be true or that are self-evidently true. Then by arguing logically, step by step, it is possible to arrive at a conclusion. If the axioms are correct and the logic is flawless, then the conclusion will be undeniable. This conclusion is the theorem.

Mathematical theorems rely on this logical process and once proven are true until the end of time. Mathematical proofs are absolute. To appreciate the value of such proofs they should be compared with their poor relation, the scientific proof. In science a hypothesis is put forward to explain a physical phenomenon. If observations of the phenomenon compare well with the hypothesis, this becomes evidence in favor of it. Furthermore, the hypothesis should not merely describe a known phenomenon, but predict the results of other phenomena. Experiments may be performed to test the predictive power of the hypothesis, and if it continues to be successful then this is even more evidence to back the hypothesis. Eventually the amount of evidence may be overwhelming and the hypothesis becomes accepted as a scientific theory.

However, the scientific theory can never be proved to the same absolute level of a mathematical theorem: It is merely considered highly likely based on the evidence available. So-called scientific proof relies on observation and perception, both of which are fallible and provide only approximations to the truth. As Bertrand Russell pointed out: "Although this may seem a paradox, all exact science is dominated by the idea of approximation." Even the most widely accepted scientific "proofs" always have a small element of doubt in them. Sometimes this doubt diminishes, although it never disappears completely, while on other occasions the proof is ultimately shown to be wrong. This weakness in scientific proof leads to scientific revolutions in which one theory that was assumed to be correct is replaced with another theory, which may be merely a refinement of the original theory, or which may be a complete contradiction.

For example, the search for the fundamental particles of matter involved each generation of physicists overturning or, at the very least, refining the theory of their predecessors. The modern quest for the building blocks of the universe started at the beginning of the nineteenth century when a series of experiments led John Dalton to suggest that everything was composed of discrete atoms, and that atoms were fundamental. At the end of the century J. J. Thomson discovered the electron, the first known subatomic particle, and therefore the atom was no longer fundamental.

During the early years of the twentieth century, physicists developed a "complete" picture of the atom — a nucleus consisting of protons and neutrons, orbited by electrons. Protons, neutrons, and electrons were proudly held up as the complete ingredients for the universe. Then cosmic ray experiments revealed the existence of other fundamental particles — pions and muons. An even greater revolution came with the discovery in 1932 of antimatter — the existence of antiprotons, antineutrons, antielectrons, etc. By this time particle physicists could not be sure how many different particles existed, but at least they could be confident that these entities were indeed fundamental. That was until the 1960s when the concept of the quark was born. The proton itself is apparently built from fractionally charged quarks, as is the neutron and the pion. In the next decade the very concept of a particle as a pointlike object may even be replaced by the idea of particles as strings. The theory is that strings a billionth of a billionth of a billionth of a billionth of a meter in length (so small that they appear pointlike) can vibrate in different ways, and each vibration gives rise to a different particle. This is analogous to Pythagoras's discovery that one string on a lyre can give rise to different notes depending on how it vibrates. The moral of the story is that physicists are continually altering their picture of the universe, if not rubbing it out and starting all over again.

The science fiction writer and futurologist Arthur C. Clarke wrote that if an eminent professor states that something is undoubtedly true, then it is likely to be proved false the next day. Scientific proof is inevitably fickle and shoddy. On the other hand, mathematical proof is absolute and devoid of doubt. Pythagoras died confident in the knowledge that his theorem, which was true in 500 B.C., would remain true for eternity.

Science is operated according to the judicial system. A theory is assumed to be true if there is enough evidence to prove it "beyond all reasonable doubt." On the other hand, mathematics does not rely on evidence from fallible experimentation, but it is built on infallible logic. This is demonstrated by the problem of the "mutilated chessboard," illustrated in Figure 3.

We have a chessboard with the two opposing corners removed, so that there are only 62 squares remaining. Now we take 31 dominoes shaped such that each domino covers exactly two squares. The question is: Is it possible to arrange the 31 dominoes so that they cover all the 62 squares on the chessboard?

There are two approaches to the problem:

(1) The scientific approach
The scientist would try to solve the problem by experimenting, and after trying out a few dozen arrangements would discover that they all fail. Eventually the scientist believes that there is enough evidence to say that the board cannot be covered. However, the scientist can never be sure that this is truly the case, because there might be some arrangement that has not been

Figure 3. The problem of the mutilated chessboard.

tried that might do the trick. There are millions of different arrangements, and it is possible to explore only a small fraction of them. The conclusion that the task is impossible is a theory based on experiment, but the scientist will have to live with the prospect that one day the theory may be overturned.

(2) The mathematical approach

The mathematician tries to answer the question by developing a logical argument that will derive a conclusion that is undoubtedly correct and that will remain unchallenged forever. One such argument is the following:

• The corners that were removed from the chessboard were

both white. Therefore there are now 32 black squares and only 30 white squares.

• Each domino covers two neighboring squares, and neighboring squares are always different in color, i.e., one black and one white.

• Therefore, no matter how they are arranged, the first 30 dominoes laid on the board must cover 30 white squares and 30 black squares.

• Consequently, this will always leave you with one domino and two black squares remaining.

• But remember, all dominoes cover two neighboring squares, and neighboring squares are opposite in color. However, the two squares remaining are the same color and so they cannot both be covered by the one remaining domino. Therefore, covering the board is impossible!

This proof shows that every possible arrangement of dominoes will fail to cover the mutilated chessboard. Similarly Pythagoras constructed a proof that shows that every possible right-angled triangle will obey his theorem. For Pythagoras the concept of mathematical proof was sacred, and it was proof that enabled the Brotherhood to discover so much. Most modern proofs are incredibly complicated and following the logic would be impossible for the layperson, but fortunately in the case of Pythagoras's theorem the argument is relatively straightforward and relies on only high-school mathematics. The proof is outlined in Appendix 1.

Pythagoras's proof is irrefutable. It shows that his theorem holds true for every right-angled triangle in the universe. The discovery was so momentous that one hundred oxen were sacrificed as an act of gratitude to the gods. The discovery was a milestone in mathematics and one of the most important breakthroughs in the history of civilization. Its significance was twofold. First, it developed the idea of proof. A proven mathematical result has a deeper truth than any other truth because it is the result of step-by-step logic. Although the philosopher Thales had already invented some primitive geometrical proofs, Pythagoras took the idea much further and was able to prove far more ingenious mathematical statements. The second consequence of Pythagoras's theorem is that it ties the abstract mathematical method to something tangible. Pythagoras showed that the truth of mathematics could be applied to the scientific world and provide it with a logical foundation. Mathematics gives science a rigorous beginning, and upon this infallible foundation scientists add inaccurate measurements and imperfect observations.

An Infinity of Triples

The Pythagorean Brotherhood invigorated mathematics with its zealous search for truth via proof. News of their success spread and yet the details of their discoveries remained a closely guarded secret. Many requested admission to the inner sanctum of knowledge, but only the most brilliant minds were accepted. One of those who was blackballed was a candidate by the name of Cylon. Cylon took exception to his humiliating rejection and twenty years later he took his revenge.

During the sixty-seventh Olympiad (510 B.C.) there was a revolt in the nearby city of Sybaris. Telys, the victorious leader of the revolt, began a barbaric campaign of persecution against the supporters of the former government, which drove many of them to seek sanctuary in Croton. Telys demanded that the traitors be returned to Sybaris to suffer their due punishment, but Milo and Pythagoras persuaded the citizens of Croton to stand up to the tyrant and protect the refugees. Telys was furious and immediately gathered an army of 300,000 men and marched on Croton, where Milo defended the city with 100,000 armed citizens. After seventy days of war Milo's supreme generalship led him to victory, and as an act of retribution he turned the course of the river Crathis upon Sybaris to flood and destroy the city.

Despite the end of the war, the city of Croton was still in turmoil because of arguments over what should be done with the spoils of war. Fearful that the lands would be given to the Pythagorean elite, the ordinary folk of Croton began to grumble. There had already been growing resentment among the masses because the secretive Brotherhood continued to withhold their discoveries, but nothing came of it until Cylon emerged as the voice of the people. Cylon preyed on the fear, paranoia, and envy of the mob and led them on a mission to destroy the most brilliant school of mathematics the world had ever seen. Milo's house and the adjoining school were surrounded, all the doors were locked and barred to prevent escape, and then the burning began. Milo fought his way out of the inferno and fled, but Pythagoras, along with many of his disciples, was killed.

Mathematics had lost its first great hero, but the Pythagorean spirit lived on. The numbers and their truths were immortal. Pythagoras had demonstrated that more than any other discipline mathematics is a subject that is not subjective. His disciples did not need their master to decide on the validity of a particular theory. A theory's truth was independent of opinion. Instead the construction of mathematical logic had become the arbiter of truth. This was the Pythagoreans' greatest contribution to civilization — a way of achieving truth that is beyond the fallibility of human judgment.

Following the death of their founder and the attack by Cylon, the Brotherhood left Croton for other cities in Magna Graecia, but the persecution continued and eventually many of them had to settle in foreign lands. This enforced migration encouraged the Pythagoreans to spread their mathematical gospel throughout the ancient world. Pythagoras's disciples set up new schools and taught their students the method of logical proof. In addition to their proof of Pythagoras's theorem, they also explained to the world the secret of finding so-called Pythagorean triples.

Pythagorean triples are combinations of three whole numbers that perfectly fit Pythagoras's equation: $x^2 + y^2 = z^2$. For example, Pythagoras's equation holds true if $x = 3$, $y = 4$, and $z = 5$:

$$3^2 + 4^2 = 5^2, \quad 9 + 16 = 25.$$

Another way to think of Pythagorean triples is in terms of rearranging squares. If one has a 3×3 square made of 9 tiles, and a 4×4 square made of 16 tiles, then all the tiles can be rearranged to form a 5×5 square made of 25 tiles, as shown in Figure 4.

The Pythagoreans wanted to find other Pythagorean triples, other squares that could be added to form a third, larger square. Another Pythagorean triple is $x = 5$, $y = 12$, and $z = 13$:

$$5^2 + 12^2 = 13^2, \quad 25 + 144 = 169.$$

A larger Pythagorean triple is $x = 99$, $y = 4,900$, and $z = 4,901$. Pythagorean triples become rarer as the numbers increase, and finding them becomes harder and harder. To discover as many triples as possible the Pythgoreans invented a methodical way of

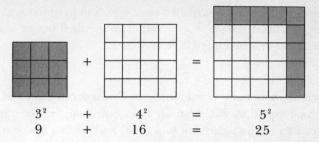

$$3^2 \quad + \quad 4^2 \quad = \quad 5^2$$
$$9 \quad + \quad 16 \quad = \quad 25$$

Figure 4. Finding whole number solutions to Pythagoras's equation can be thought of in terms of finding two squares that can be added together to form a third square. For example, a square made of 9 tiles can be added to a square of 16 tiles, and rearranged to form a third square made of 25 tiles.

finding them, and in so doing they also demonstrated that there are an infinite number of Pythagorean triples.

From Pythagoras's Theorem to Fermat's Last Theorem

Pythagoras's theorem and its infinity of triples was discussed in E. T. Bell's *The Last Problem*, the library book that caught the attention of the young Andrew Wiles. Although the Brotherhood had achieved an almost complete understanding of Pythagorean triples, Wiles soon discovered that this apparently innocent equation, $x^2 + y^2 = z^2$, has a darker side — Bell's book described the existence of a mathematical monster.

In Pythagoras's equation the three numbers, x, y, and z, are all squared (i.e., $x^2 = x \times x$):

$$x^2 + y^2 = z^2.$$

However, the book described a sister equation in which x, y, and z are all cubed (i.e., $x^3 = x \times x \times x$). The so-called power of x in this equation is no longer 2, but rather 3:

$$x^3 + y^3 = z^3.$$

Finding whole number solutions, i.e., Pythagorean triples, to the original equation was relatively easy, but changing the power from 2 to 3 (from a square to a cube) and finding whole number solutions to the sister equation appears to be impossible. Generations of mathematicians have failed to find numbers that fit the cubed equation perfectly.

With the original "squared" equation, the challenge was to rearrange the tiles in two squares to form a third, larger square. In the "cubed" version the challenge is to rearrange two cubes made of building blocks, to form a third, larger cube. Apparently, no matter what cubes are chosen to begin with, when they are combined the result is either a complete cube with some extra blocks left over, or an incomplete cube. The nearest that anyone has come to a perfect rearrangement is one in which there is one building block too many or too few. For example, if we begin with the cubes 6^3 (x^3) and 8^3 (y^3) and rearrange the building blocks, then we are only one short of making a complete $9 \times 9 \times 9$ cube, as shown in Figure 5.

Finding three numbers that fit the cubed equation perfectly seems to be impossible. That is to say, there appear to be no whole number solutions to the equation

$$x^3 + y^3 = z^3.$$

Furthermore, if the power is changed from 3 (cubed) to any higher number n (i.e., 4, 5, 6, ...), then finding a solution seems

$$6^3 \quad + \quad 8^3 \quad = \quad 9^3 - 1$$
$$216 \quad + \quad 512 \quad = \quad 729 - 1$$

Figure 5. Is it possible to add the building blocks from one cube to another cube, to form a third, larger, cube? In this case a $6 \times 6 \times 6$ cube added to an $8 \times 8 \times 8$ cube doesn't have quite enough building blocks to form a $9 \times 9 \times 9$ cube. There are 216 (6^3) building blocks in the first cube, and 512 (8^3) in the second. The total is 728 building blocks, which is 1 short of 9^3.

equally impossible. There appear to be no whole number solutions to the more general equation

$$x^n + y^n = z^n \text{ for } n \text{ greater than 2.}$$

By merely changing the 2 in Pythagoras's equation to any higher number, finding whole number solutions turns from being relatively simple to being mind-bogglingly difficult. In fact, the great seventeenth-century Frenchman Pierre de Fermat made the astonishing claim that the reason why nobody could find any solutions was that no solutions existed.

Fermat was one of the most brilliant and intriguing mathematicians in history. He could not have checked the infinity of numbers, but he was absolutely sure that no combination existed that would fit the equation perfectly because his claim was based on proof. Like Pythagoras, who did not have to check every triangle to demonstrate the validity of his theorem, Fermat did not have to check every number to show the validity of his theorem. Fermat's Last Theorem, as it is known, stated that

$$x^n + y^n = z^n$$

has no whole number solutions for n greater than 2.

As Wiles read each chapter of Bell's book, he learned how Fermat had become fascinated by Pythagoras's work and had eventually come to study the perverted form of Pythagoras's equation. He then read how Fermat had claimed that even if all the mathematicians in the world spent eternity looking for a solution to the equation they would fail to find one. He must have eagerly turned the pages, relishing the thought of examining the proof of Fermat's Last Theorem. However, the proof was not there. It was not anywhere. Bell ended the book by stating that the proof had been lost long ago. There was no hint of what it might have been, no clues as to the proof's construction or derivation. Wiles found himself puzzled, infuriated, and intrigued. He was in good company.

For over 300 years many of the greatest mathematicians had tried to rediscover Fermat's lost proof and failed. As each generation failed, the next became even more frustrated and determined. In 1742, almost a century after Fermat's death, the Swiss mathematician Leonhard Euler asked his friend Clêrot to search Fermat's house in case some vital scrap of paper still remained. No clues were ever found as to what Fermat's proof might have been.

Fermat's Last Theorem, a problem that had captivated mathematicians for centuries, captured the imagination of the young Andrew Wiles. In Milton Road Library, ten-year-old

Wiles stared at the most infamous problem in mathematics, undaunted by the knowledge that the most brilliant minds on the planet had failed to rediscover the proof. Young Wiles immediately set to work using all his textbook techniques to try to recreate the proof. Perhaps he could find something that everyone else, except Fermat, had overlooked. He dreamed he could shock the world.

Thirty years later Andrew Wiles stood in the auditorium of the Isaac Newton Institute. He scribbled on the board and then, struggling to contain his glee, stared at his audience. The lecture was reaching its climax and the audience knew it. One or two of them had smuggled cameras into the lecture room and flashes peppered his concluding remarks.

With the chalk in his hand he turned to the board for the last time. The final few lines of logic completed the proof. For the first time in over three centuries Fermat's challenge had been met. A few more cameras flashed to capture the historic moment. Wiles wrote up the statement of Fermat's Last Theorem, turned toward the audience, and said modestly: "I think I'll stop here."

Two hundred mathematicians clapped and cheered in celebration. Even those who had anticipated the result grinned in disbelief. After three decades Andrew Wiles believed he had achieved his dream, and after seven years of isolation he had revealed his secret calculation. While a general mood of euphoria filled the Newton Institute, everybody realized that the proof still had to be rigorously checked by a team of independent referees. However, as Wiles enjoyed the moment, nobody could have predicted the controversy that would evolve in the months ahead.

Pierre de Fermat

2

The Riddler

· · · · · · · · · · · · ·

> "Do you know," the Devil confided, "not even the best
> mathematicians on other planets — all far ahead of yours —
> have solved it? Why, there's a chap on Saturn — he looks
> something like a mushroom on stilts — who solves partial
> differential equations mentally; and even he's given up."
>
> Arthur Porges, "The Devil and Simon Flagg"

Pierre de Fermat was born on August 20, 1601, in the town of
Beaumont-de-Lomagne in southwest France. His father, Domin-
ique Fermat, was a wealthy leather merchant, and so Pierre was
fortunate enough to enjoy a privileged education at the
Franciscan monastery of Grandselve, followed by a stint at the
University of Toulouse. There is no record of the young Fermat
showing any particular brilliance in mathematics.

Pressure from his family steered Fermat toward a career in the
civil service, and in 1631 he was appointed *conseiller au Parlement
de Toulouse*, a councillor at the Chamber of Petitions. If locals
wanted to petition the King on any matter they first had to
convince Fermat or one of his associates of the importance of
their request. The councillors provided the vital link between
the province and Paris. As well as liaising between the locals
and the monarch, the councillors made sure that royal decrees
emanating from the capital were implemented back in the

regions. Fermat was an efficient civil servant, who by all accounts carried out his duties in a considerate and merciful manner.

Fermat's additional duties included service in the judiciary, and he was senior enough to deal with the most severe cases. An account of his work is given by the English mathematician Sir Kenelm Digby. Digby had requested to see Fermat, but in a letter to a mutual colleague, John Wallis, he reveals that the Frenchman had been occupied with pressing judicial matters, thus excluding the possibility of a meeting:

> It is true that I had exactly hit the date of the displacement of the judges of Castres to Toulouse, where he [Fermat] is the Supreme Judge to the Sovereign Court of Parliament; and since then he has been occupied with capital cases of great importance, in which he has finished by imposing a sentence that has made a great stir; it concerned the condemnation of a priest, who had abused his functions, to be burned at the stake. This affair has just finished and the execution has followed.

Fermat corresponded regularly with Digby and Wallis. Later we will see that the letters were often less than friendly, but they provide vital insights into Fermat's daily life, including his academic work.

Fermat rose rapidly within the ranks of the civil service and became a member of the social elite, entitling him to use *de* as part of his name. His promotion was not necessarily the result of ambition, but rather a matter of health. The plague was raging throughout Europe, and those who survived were elevated to fill the places of those who died. Even Fermat suffered a serious bout of plague in 1652, and was so ill that his friend Bernard Medon announced his death to several colleagues. Soon after he corrected himself in a report to the Dutchman Nicholas Heinsius:

I informed you earlier of the death of Fermat. He is still alive, and we no longer fear for his health, even though we had counted him among the dead a short time ago. The plague no longer rages among us.

In addition to the health risks of seventeenth-century France, Fermat had to survive the political dangers. His appointment to the Parliament of Toulouse came just three years after Cardinal Richelieu was promoted to first minister of France. This was an era of plotting and intrigue, and everyone involved in the running of the state, even at local government level, had to take care not to become embroiled in the machinations of the Cardinal. Fermat adopted the strategy of performing duties efficiently without drawing attention to himself. He had no great political ambition, and did his best to avoid the rough and tumble of parliament. Instead he devoted all his spare energy to mathematics and, when not sentencing priests to be burnt at the stake, Fermat dedicated himself to his hobby. Fermat was a true amateur academic, a man whom E. T. Bell called the "Prince of Amateurs." But he was so talented that when Julian Coolidge wrote *Mathematics of Great Amateurs*, he excluded Fermat on the grounds that he was "so really great that he should count as a professional."

At the start of the seventeenth century, mathematics was still recovering from the Dark Ages and was not a highly regarded subject. Similarly mathematicians were not treated with great respect and most of them had to fund their own studies. For example, Galileo was unable to study mathematics at the University of Pisa and was forced to seek private tuition. Indeed, the only institute in Europe to actively encourage mathematicians was Oxford University, which had established the Savilian Chair of Geometry in 1619. So to some extent it is true to say that most seventeenth-century mathematicians were amateurs, but Fermat was an extreme case. Living far from Paris, he was isolated from the small community of mathematicians that did exist, which included such figures as Pascal, Gassendi, Roberval, Beaugrand, and most notably Father Marin Mersenne.

Although Father Mersenne made few breakthroughs in the subject, he nonetheless played a major role in seventeenth-century mathematics. After joining the order of Minims in 1611, Mersenne studied mathematics and then taught the subject to other monks and to nuns at the Minim convent at Nevers. Eight years later he moved to Paris to join the Minims de l'Annociade, close to the Place Royale, a natural gathering place for intellectuals. Inevitably, Mersenne met with the other mathemeticians, but he was saddened by their reluctance to talk to him or to each other.

The secretive nature of the Parisian mathematicians was a tradition that had been passed down from the cossists of the sixteenth century. The cossists were experts in calculations of all kinds and were employed by merchants and businessmen to solve complex accounting problems. Their name derives from the Italian word *cosa*, meaning "thing," because they used symbols to represent an unknown quantity, similar to the way mathematicians use x today. All professional problem-solvers of this era invented their own clever methods for performing calculations and would do their utmost to keep these methods secret in order to maintain their reputation as the only person capable of solving a particular problem. The secretive nature of mathematicians continued right up until the end of the nineteenth century, and as we shall see later, there are even examples of secret geniuses working in the twentieth century.

When Father Mersenne arrived in Paris he was determined to fight against the ethos of secrecy and tried to encourage mathematicians to exchange their ideas and build upon each other's work. The monk arranged regular meetings and his group later formed the core of the French Academy. When anyone refused to attend, Mersenne would pass on to the group whatever he could by revealing letters and papers — even if they had been sent to him in confidence. It was not ethical behavior for a man of the cloth, but he justified it on the grounds that the exchange of information would benefit mathematics and mankind. These acts of indiscretion naturally caused bitter arguments between the well-meaning monk and the taciturn prima donnas, and eventually destroyed Mersenne's relationship with Descartes, which had lasted since the two men had studied together at the Jesuit College of La Flèche. Mersenne had revealed philosophical writings by Descartes that were liable to offend the Church, but to his credit he did defend Descartes against theological attacks, as in fact he had done earlier in the case of Galileo.

Mersenne traveled throughout France and farther afield, spreading news of the latest discoveries. In his travels he would make a point of meeting up with Pierre de Fermat and, indeed, seems to have been Fermat's only regular contact with another mathematician. Mersenne's influence on this Prince of Amateurs must have been significant, and when he was unable to travel Mersenne would maintain his relationship with Fermat and others by writing prolifically. After Mersenne's death his room was found stacked with letters written by seventy-eight different correspondents.

Despite the encouragement of Father Mersenne, Fermat steadfastly refused to reveal his proofs. Publication and recognition meant nothing to him, and he was satisfied with the simple pleasure of being able to create new theorems undisturbed. However, the shy and retiring genius did have a mischievous streak, which, when combined with his secrecy, meant that when he did some-times communicate with other mathematicians it was only to tease them. He would write letters stating his most recent theorem without providing the accompanying proof. Then he would chal-lenge his contemporaries to find the proof. The fact that he would never reveal his own proofs caused a great deal of frustration. René Descartes called Fermat a "braggart" and the Englishman John Wallis referred to him as "that damned Frenchman." Unfortu-nately for the English, Fermat took particular pleasure in toying with his cousins across the Channel.

As well as having the satisfaction of annoying his colleagues, Fermat's habit of stating a problem but hiding its solution did have more practical motivations. First, it meant that he did not have to waste time fully fleshing out his methods; instead he could rapidly proceed to his next conquest. Furthermore, he did not have to suffer jealous nit-picking. Once published, proofs would be exam-ined and argued over by everyone and anyone who knew anything about the subject. When Blaise Pascal pressed him to publish some of his work, the recluse replied: "Whatever of my work is judged worthy of publication, I do not want my name to appear there." Fermat was the secretive genius who sacrificed fame in order not to be distracted by petty questions from his critics.

This exchange of letters with Pascal, the only occasion when Fermat discussed ideas with anyone but Mersenne, concerned the creation of an entirely new branch of mathematics — probability theory. The mathematical hermit was introduced to the subject by Pascal, and so, despite his desire for isolation, he felt obliged to maintain a dialogue. Together Fermat and Pascal would discover the first proofs and cast-iron certainties in probability theory, a subject that is inherently uncertain. Pascal's interest in the subject had been sparked by a professional Parisian gambler, Antoine

Gombaud, the Chevalier de Méré, who had posed a problem that concerned a game of chance called *points*. The game involves winning points on the roll of a dice, and whichever player is the first to earn a certain number of points is the winner and takes the prize money.

Gombaud had been involved in a game of points with a fellow gambler when they were forced to abandon the game halfway through, owing to a pressing engagement. The problem then arose as to what to do with the prize money. The simple solution would have been to have given all the money to the competitor with the most points, but Gombaud asked Pascal if there was a fairer way to divide the money. Pascal was asked to calculate the probability of each player winning had the game continued and assuming that both players would have had an equal chance of winning subsequent points. The prize money could then be split according to these calculated probabilities.

Prior to the seventeenth century the laws of probability were defined by the intuition and experience of gamblers, but Pascal entered into an exchange of letters with Fermat with the aim of discovering the mathematical rules that more accurately describe the laws of chance. Three centuries later Bertrand Russell would comment on this apparent oxymoron: "How dare we speak of the laws of chance? Is not chance the antithesis of all law?"

The Frenchmen analyzed Gombaud's question and soon realized that it was a relatively trivial problem that could be solved by rigorously defining all the potential outcomes of the game and assigning an individual probability to each one. Both Pascal and Fermat were capable of independently solving Gombaud's problem, but their collaboration speeded up the discovery of a solution and led them to a deeper exploration of other more subtle and sophisticated questions related to probability.

Probability problems are sometimes controversial because the mathematical answer, the true answer, is often contrary to what intuition might suggest. This failure of intuition is perhaps surprising because "survival of the fittest" ought to provide a strong evolutionary pressure in favor of a brain naturally capable of analyzing questions of probability. You can imagine our ancestors stalking a young deer, and weighing up whether or not to attack. What is the risk that a stag is nearby, ready to defend its offspring and injure its assailant? On the other hand, what is the chance that a better opportunity for a meal might arise if this one is judged too risky? A talent for analyzing probability should be part of our genetic make-up, and yet often our intuition misleads us.

One of the most counterintuitive probability problems concerns the likelihood of sharing birthdays. Imagine a soccer field with 23 people on it, two teams of 11 players and the referee. What is the probability that any two of those 23 people share the same birthday? With 23 people and 365 birthdays to chose from, it would seem highly unlikely that anybody would share the same birthday. If asked to put a figure on it most people would guess a probability of perhaps 10% at most. In fact, the actual answer is just over 50% — that is to say, on the balance of probability, it is more likely than not that two people on the field will share the same birthday.

The reason for this high probability is that what matters more than the number of people is the number of ways people can be paired. When we look for a shared birthday, we need to look at pairs of people, not individuals. Whereas there are only 23 people on the field, there are 253 pairs of people. For example, the first person can be paired with any of the other 22 people, giving 22 pairings to start with. Then the second person can be paired with any of the remaining 21 people (we have already counted the second person paired with the first person so the number of possible pairings is reduced by one), giving an additional 21 pairings. Then the third person can be paired with any of the remaining 20 people, giving an additional 20 pairings, and so on until we reach a total of 253 pairs.

There are more steps to calculating the exact probability, but already with 253 pairs and 365 possible birthdays, it no longer seems so unreasonable that the probability of a shared birthday is significant. In fact the probability of a shared birthday within a group of 23 people is 50.7%. This seems intuitively wrong, and yet it is mathematically undeniable. Strange probabilities such as this are exactly what bookmakers and gamblers rely on in order to exploit the unwary.

Fermat and Pascal founded the essential rules that govern all games of chance and that can be used by gamblers to define perfect playing and betting strategies. Furthermore, these laws of probability have found applications in a whole series of situations, ranging from speculating on the stock market to estimating the probability of a nuclear accident. Pascal was even convinced that he could use his theories to justify a belief in God. He stated that "the excitement that a gambler feels when making a bet is equal to the amount he might win multiplied by the probability of winning it." He then argued that the possible prize of eternal happiness has an infinite value and that the probability of entering heaven by leading a virtuous life, no matter how small, is certainly finite. Therefore, according to Pascal's definition, religion was a game of infinite excitement and one worth playing, because multiplying an infinite prize by a finite probability results in infinity.

As well as sharing the parentage of probability theory, Fermat was deeply involved in the founding of another area of mathematics, calculus. Calculus is the ability to calculate the rate of change (known as the derivative) of one quantity with respect to another. For example, the rate of change of distance with respect to time is better known simply as velocity. For mathematicians the quantities tend to be abstract and intangible, but the consequences of Fermat's work were to revolutionize science. Fermat's mathematics enabled scientists to better understand the concept of velocity and its relation to other fundamental quantities such as acceleration — the rate of change of velocity with respect to time.

For centuries Isaac Newton was thought to have discovered calculus independently and without any knowledge of Fermat's work, but in 1934 Louis Trenchard Moore discovered a note that set the record straight and gave Fermat the credit he deserves. Newton wrote that he developed his calculus based on "Monsieur Fermat's method of drawing tangents." Ever since the seventeenth century calculus has been used to describe Newton's law of gravity and his laws of mechanics, which depend on distance, velocity, and acceleration.

The discovery of calculus and probability theory would have been more than enough to earn Fermat a place in the mathematicians' hall of fame, but his greatest achievement was in yet another branch of mathematics. While calculus has since been used to send rockets to the moon, and while probability theory has been used for risk assessment by insurance companies, Fermat's greatest love was for a subject that is largely useless — the theory of numbers. Fermat was driven by an obsession to understand the properties of and the relationships between numbers. This is the purest and most ancient form of mathematics, and Fermat was building on a body of knowledge that had been handed down to him from Pythagoras.

The Evolution of Number Theory

After Pythagoras's death the concept of mathematical proof rapidly spread across the civilized world, and two centuries after his School was burnt to the ground the hub of mathematical study had moved from Croton to the city of Alexandria. In 332 B.C., having conquered Greece, Asia Minor, and Egypt, Alexander the Great decided that he would build a capital city that would be the most magnificent in the world. Alexandria was indeed a spectacular metropolis but not immediately a center of learning. It was only when Alexander died and Ptolemy I ascended the throne of Egypt that Alexandria became home to the world's first-ever university. Mathematicians and other intellectuals flocked to Ptolemy's city of culture, and although they were certainly drawn by the reputation of the university, the main attraction was the Alexandrian Library.

The Library was the idea of Demetrius Phalaerus, an unpopular orator who had been forced to flee Athens, and who eventually found sanctuary in Alexandria. He persuaded Ptolemy to gather together all the great books, assuring him that the great minds would follow. Once the tomes of Egypt and Greece had been installed, agents scoured Europe and Asia Minor in search of further volumes of knowledge. Even tourists to Alexandria could not escape the voracious appetite of the Library. Upon entering the city, their books were confiscated and taken to the scribes. The books were copied so that while the original was donated to the Library, a duplicate could graciously be given to the original owner. This meticulous replication service for ancient travelers gives today's historians some hope that a copy of a great lost text will one day turn up in an attic somewhere in the world. In 1906 J. L. Heiberg discovered in Constantinople just such a manuscript, *The Method*, which contained some of Archimedes' original writings.

Ptolemy's dream of building a treasure house of knowledge lived on after his death, and by the time a few more Ptolemys had ascended the throne the Library contained over 600,000 books. Mathematicians could learn everything in the known world by studying at Alexandria, and there to teach them were the most famous academics. The first head of the mathematics department was none other than Euclid.

Euclid was born in about 330 B.C. Like Pythagoras, Euclid believed in the search for mathematical truth for its own sake and did not look for applications in his work. One story tells of a student who questioned him about the use of the mathematics he was learning. Upon completing the lesson, Euclid turned to his slave and said, "Give the boy a penny since he desires to profit from all that he learns." The student was then expelled.

Euclid devoted much of his life to writing the *Elements,* the most successful textbook in history. Until this century it was also the second-best-selling book in the world after the Bible. The *Elements* consists of thirteen books, some of which are devoted to Euclid's own work, and the remainder being a compilation of all the mathematical knowledge of the age, including two volumes devoted entirely to the works of the Pythagorean Brotherhood. In the centuries since Pythagoras, mathematicians had invented a variety of logical techniques that could be applied in different circumstances, and Euclid skillfully employed them all in the *Elements.* In particular Euclid exploited a logical weapon known as *reductio ad absurdum,* or proof by contradiction. The approach revolves around the perverse idea of trying to prove that a theorem is true by first assuming that the theorem is false. The mathematician then explores the logical consequences of the theorem being false. At some point along the chain of logic there is a contradiction (e.g., $2 + 2 = 5$). Mathematics abhors a contradiction, and therefore the original theorem cannot be false, i.e., it must be true.

The English mathematician G. H. Hardy encapsulated the spirit of proof by contradiction in his book *A Mathematician's Apology:* "Reductio ad absurdum, which Euclid loved so much, is one of a mathematician's finest weapons. It is a far finer gambit than any chess play: a chess player may offer the sacrifice of a pawn or even a piece, but a mathematician offers the game."

One of Euclid's most famous proofs by contradiction established the existence of so-called *irrational numbers*. It is suspected that irrational numbers were originally discovered by the Pythagorean Brotherhood centuries earlier, but the concept was so abhorrent to Pythagoras that he denied their existence.

When Pythagoras claimed that the universe is governed by numbers he meant whole numbers and ratios of whole numbers (fractions), together known as rational numbers. An irrational number is a number that is neither a whole number nor a fraction, and this is what made it so horrific to Pythagoras. In fact, irrational numbers are so strange that they cannot be written down as decimals, even recurring decimals. A recurring decimal such as $0.111111\ldots$ is in fact a fairly straightforward number, and is equivalent to the fraction $\frac{1}{9}$. The fact that the '1' repeats itself forever means that the decimal has a very simple and regular pattern. This regularity, despite the fact that it continues to infinity, means that the decimal can be rewritten as a fraction. If you attempt to express an irrational number as a decimal you end up with a number that continues forever with no regular or consistent pattern.

The concept of an irrational number was a tremendous breakthrough. Mathematicians were looking beyond the whole numbers and fractions around them, and discovering, or perhaps inventing, new ones. The nineteenth-century mathematician Leopold Kronecker said, "God made the integers; all the rest is the work of man."

The most famous irrational number is π. In schools it is some-times approximated by $3\frac{1}{7}$ or 3.14; however, the true value of π is nearer 3.14159265358979323846, but even this is only an approxi-mation. In fact, π can never be written down exactly, because the decimal places go on forever without any pattern. A beautiful feature of this random pattern is that it can be computed using an equation that is supremely regular:

$$\pi = 4\left(\frac{1}{1} - \frac{1}{3} + \frac{1}{5} - \frac{1}{7} + \frac{1}{9} - \frac{1}{11} + \frac{1}{13} - \frac{1}{15} + \ldots\right) \quad .$$

By calculating the first few terms, you can obtain a very rough value for π, but by calculating more and more terms an increasingly accurate value is achieved. Although knowing π to 39 decimal places is sufficient to calculate the circumference of the universe accurate to the radius of a hydrogen atom, this has not prevented computer scientists from calculating π to as many decimal places as possible. The current record is held by Yasumasa Kanada of the University of Tokyo, who calculated π to six billion decimal places in 1996. Recently rumors have suggested that the Russian Chudnovsky brothers in New York have calculated π to eight billion decimal places and that they are aiming to reach a trillion decimal places. However, even if Kanada or the Chudnovsky brothers carried on calculating until their computers sapped all the energy in the universe, they would still not have found the exact value of π. It is easy to appreciate why Pythagoras conspired to hide the existence of these mathematical beasts.

When Euclid dared to confront the issue of irrationality in the tenth volume of the *Elements* the goal was to prove that there could be a number that could never be written as a fraction. Instead of trying to prove that π is irrational, he examined the square root of two, $\sqrt{2}$ — the number that when multiplied by itself is equal to two. In order to prove that $\sqrt{2}$ could not be written as a fraction Euclid used *reductio ad absurdum* and began by assuming that it could be written as a fraction. He then demonstrated that this hypothetical fraction could be simplified. (Simplification of a fraction means, for example, that the fraction $\frac{8}{12}$ can be simplified to $\frac{4}{6}$ by dividing top and bottom by 2. In turn $\frac{4}{6}$ can be simplified to $\frac{2}{3}$, which cannot be simplified any further and therefore the fraction is then said to be in its simplest form.) Furthermore, Euclid showed that his simplified fraction, which still was supposed to represent $\sqrt{2}$, could be simplified not just once but over and over again an infinite number of times without ever reducing to its simplest form. This is absurd because all fractions must eventually have a simplest form, and therefore the hypothetical fraction cannot exist. Therefore $\sqrt{2}$ cannot be written as a fraction and is irrational. A more detailed outline of Euclid's proof is given in Appendix 2.

By using proof by contradiction Euclid was able to prove the existence of irrational numbers. For the first time, numbers had taken on a new and more abstract quality. Until this point in history all numbers could be expressed as whole numbers or fractions, but Euclid's irrational numbers defied representation in the traditional manner. There is no way to describe the number equal to the square root of two than by expressing it as $\sqrt{2}$, because it cannot be written as a fraction and any attempt to write it as a decimal could only ever be an approximation, e.g., 1.414213562373 . . .

For Pythagoras, the beauty of mathematics was the idea that rational numbers (whole numbers and fractions) could explain all natural phenomena. This guiding philosophy blinded Pythagoras to the existence of irrational numbers and may even have led to the execution of one of his pupils. One story claims that a young student by the name of Hippasus was idly toying with the number $\sqrt{2}$, attempting to find the equivalent fraction. Eventually he came to realize that no such fraction existed, i.e., that $\sqrt{2}$ is an irrational number. Hippasus must have been overjoyed by his discovery, but his master was not. Pythagoras had defined the universe in terms of rational numbers, and the existence of irrational numbers brought his ideal into question. The consequence of Hippasus's insight should have been a period of discussion and contemplation during which Pythagoras ought to have come to terms with this new source of numbers. However, Pythagoras was unwilling to accept that he was wrong, but at the same time he was unable to destroy Hippasus's argument by the power of logic. To his eternal shame he sentenced Hippasus to death by drowning.

The father of logic and the mathematical method had resorted to force rather than admit he was wrong. Pythagoras's denial of irrational numbers is his most disgraceful act and perhaps the worst tragedy of Greek mathematics. It was only after his death that irrationals could be safely resurrected.

Although Euclid clearly had an interest in the theory of numbers, it was not his greatest contribution to mathematics. Euclid's true passion was geometry, and of the thirteen volumes that make up the *Elements,* books I to VI concentrate on plane (two-dimensional) geometry and books XI to XIII deal with solid (three-dimensional) geometry. It is such a complete body of knowledge that the contents of the *Elements* would form the geometry syllabus in schools and universities for the next two thousand years.

The mathematician who compiled the equivalent text for number theory was Diophantus of Alexandria, the last champion of the Greek mathematical tradition. Although Diophantus's achievements in number theory are well documented in his books, virtually nothing else is known about this formidable mathematician. His place of birth is unknown and his arrival in Alexandria could have been anytime within a five-century window. In his writings Diophantus quotes Hypsicles and therefore he must have lived after 150 B.C.; on the other hand, his own work is quoted by Theon of Alexandria and therefore he must have lived before A.D. 364. A date around A.D. 250 is generally accepted as being a sensible estimate. Appropriately for a problem-solver, the one detail of Diophantus's life that has survived is in the form of a riddle said to have been carved on his tomb:

> God granted him to be a boy for the sixth part of his life, and adding a twelfth part to this, He clothed his cheeks with down; He lit him the light of wedlock after a seventh part, and five years after his marriage He granted him a son. Alas! late-born wretched child; after attaining the measure of half his father's full life, chill Fate took him. After consoling his grief by this science of numbers for four years he ended his life.

The challenge is to calculate Diophantus's life span. The answer can be found in Appendix 3.

This riddle is an example of the sort of problem that Diophantus relished. His specialty was tackling questions that required whole number solutions, and today such questions are referred to as Diophantine problems. He spent his career in Alexandria collecting well-understood problems and inventing new ones, and then compiled them all into a major treatise entitled *Arithmetica*. Of the thirteen books that made up the *Arithmetica*, only six would survive the turmoils of the Dark Ages and go on to inspire the Renaissance mathematicians, including Pierre de Fermat. The remaining seven books would be lost during a series of tragic events that would send mathematics back to the age of the Babylonians.

During the centuries between Euclid and Diophantus, Alexandria remained the intellectual capital of the civilized world, but

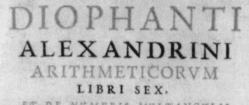

DIOPHANTI
ALEXANDRINI
ARITHMETICORVM
LIBRI SEX.
ET DE NVMERIS MVLTANGVLIS
LIBER VNVS.

Nunc primùm Græcè & Latinè editi, atque absolutissimis
Commentariis illustrati.

AVCTORE CLAVDIO GASPARE BACHETO
MEZIRIACO SEBVSIANO. V. C.

LVTETIAE PARISIORVM,
Sumptibus HIERONYMI DROVART, via Iacobæa,
sub Scuto Solari.

M. DC. XXI.
CVM PRIVILEGIO REGIS.

The frontispiece of Claude Gaspar Bachet's translation of Diophantus's *Arithmetica*, published in 1621. This book became Fermat's bible and inspired much of his work.

throughout this period the city was continually under threat from foreign armies. The first major attack occurred in 47 B.C., when Julius Caesar attempted to overthrow Cleopatra by setting fire to the Alexandrian fleet. The Library, which was located near the harbor, also caught alight, and hundreds of thousands of books were destroyed. Fortunately for mathematics Cleopatra appreciated the importance of knowledge and was determined to restore the Library to its former glory. Mark Antony realized that the way to an intellectual's heart is via her library, and so marched to the city of Pergamum. This city had already initiated a library that it hoped would provide it with the best collection in the world, but instead Mark Antony transplanted the entire stock to Egypt, restoring the supremacy of Alexandria.

For the next four centuries the Library continued to accumulate books until in A.D. 389 it received the first of two fatal blows, both the result of religious bigotry. The Christian Emperor Theodosius ordered Theophilus, Bishop of Alexandria, to destroy all pagan monuments. Unfortunately when Cleopatra rebuilt and restocked the Library, she decided to house it in the Temple of Serapis, and so the Library became caught up in the destruction of icons and altars. The "pagan" scholars attempted to save six centuries' worth of knowledge, but before they could do anything they were butchered by the Christian mob. The descent into the Dark Ages had begun.

A few precious copies of the most vital books survived the Christian onslaught and scholars continued to visit Alexandria in search of knowledge. Then, in 642, a Moslem attack succeeded where the Christians had failed. When asked what should be done with the Library, the victorious Caliph Omar commanded that those books that were contrary to the Koran should be destroyed, and furthermore those books that conformed to the Koran were superfluous and they too must be destroyed. The manuscripts were used to stoke the furnaces that heated the public baths, and Greek mathematics went up in smoke. It is not surprising that most of Diophantus's work was destroyed; in fact it is a miracle that six volumes of the *Arithmetica* managed to survive the tragedy of Alexandria.

For the next thousand years mathematics in the West was in the doldrums, and only a handful of luminaries in India and Arabia kept the subject alive. They copied the formulae described in the surviving manuscripts of Greece and then began to reinvent for themselves many of the theorems that had been lost. They also added new elements to mathematics, including the number zero.

In modern mathematics zero performs two functions. First, it allows us to distinguish between numbers like 52 and 502. In a system where the position of a number denotes its value, a symbol is needed to confirm an empty position. For instance, 52 represents 5 times ten plus 2 times one, whereas 502 represents 5 times a hundred plus 0 times ten plus 2 times one, and the zero is crucial for removing any ambiguity. Even the Babylonians in the third millennium B.C. appreciated the use of zero to avoid confusion, and the Greeks adopted their idea, using a circular symbol similar to the one we use today. However, zero has a more subtle and deeper significance that was fully appreciated only several centuries later by the mathematicians of India. The Hindus recognized that zero had an independent existence beyond the mere spacing role among the other numbers — zero was a number in its own right. It represented a quantity of nothing. For the first time the abstract concept of nothingness had been given a tangible symbolic representation.

This may seem a trivial step forward to the modern reader, but the deeper meaning of the zero symbol had been ignored by all the ancient Greek philosophers, including Aristotle. He had argued that the number zero should be outlawed because it disrupted the consistency of the other numbers — dividing any ordinary number by zero led to an incomprehensible result. By the sixth century the Indian mathematicians no longer brushed this problem under the rug, and the seventh-century scholar Brahmagupta was sophisticated enough to use division by zero as a definition for infinity.

While Europe had abandoned the noble search for truth, India and Arabia were consolidating the knowledge that had been smuggled out of the embers of Alexandria and were reinterpreting it in a new and more eloquent language. As well as adding zero to the mathematical vocabulary, they replaced the primitive Greek symbols and cumbersome Roman numerals with the counting system that has now been universally adopted. Once again, this might seem like an absurdly humble step forward, but try multiplying CLV by DCI and you will appreciate the significance of the breakthrough. The equivalent task of multiplying 155 by 601 is a good deal simpler. The growth of any discipline depends on the ability to communicate and develop ideas, and this in turn relies on a language that is sufficiently detailed and flexible. The ideas of Pythagoras and Euclid were no less elegant for their awkward expression, but translated into the symbols of Arabia they would blossom and give fruit to newer and richer concepts.

In the tenth century the French scholar Gerbert of Aurillac learned the new counting system from the Moors of Spain and through his teaching positions at churches and schools throughout Europe he was able to introduce the new system to the West. In 999 he was elected Pope Sylvester II, an appointment that allowed him to further encourage the use of Indo-Arabic numerals. Although the efficiency of the system revolutionized accounting and was rapidly adopted by merchants, it did little to inspire a revival in European mathematics.

The vital turning point for Western mathematics did not occur until 1453 when the Turks ransacked Constantinople. During the intervening years the manuscripts that had survived the desecration of Alexandria had congregated in Constantinople, but once again they were threatened with destruction. Byzantine scholars fled westward with whatever texts they could preserve. Having survived the onslaught of Caesar, Bishop Theophilus, Caliph Omar, and now the Turks, a few precious volumes of the *Arithmetica* made their way back to Europe. Diophantus was destined for the desk of Pierre de Fermat.

Birth of a Riddle

Fermat's judicial responsibilities occupied a great deal of his time, but what little leisure he had was devoted entirely to mathematics. This was partly because judges in seventeenth-century France were discouraged from socializing on the grounds that friends and acquaintances might one day be called before the court. Fraternizing with the locals would only lead to favoritism. Isolated from the rest of Toulouse's high society, Fermat could concentrate on his hobby.

There is no record of Fermat ever being inspired by a mathematical tutor; instead it was a copy of the *Arithmetica* that became his mentor. The *Arithmetica* sought to describe the theory of numbers, as it was in Diophantus's time, via a series of problems and solutions. In effect Diophantus was presenting Fermat with one thousand years' worth of mathematical understanding. In one book Fermat could find the entire knowledge of numbers as constructed by the likes of Pythagoras and Euclid. The theory of numbers had stood still ever since the barbaric burning of Alexandria, but now Fermat was ready to resume study of the most fundamental of mathematical disciplines.

The *Arithmetica* that inspired Fermat was a Latin translation made by Claude Gaspar Bachet de Méziriac, reputedly the most learned man in all of France. As well as being a brilliant linguist, poet, and classics scholar, Bachet had a passion for mathematical puzzles. His first publication was a compilation of puzzles entitled *Problemes plaisans et délectables qui se font par les nombres*, which included river-crossing problems, a liquid-pouring problem, and several think-of-a-number tricks. One of the questions posed was a problem about weights:

> What is the least number of weights that can be used on a set of scales
> to weigh any whole number of kilograms from 1 to 40?

Bachet had a cunning solution that shows that it is possible to achieve this task with only four weights. His solution is given in Appendix 4.

Although he was merely a mathematical dilettante, Bachet's interest in puzzles was enough for him to realize that Diophantus's list of problems was on a higher plane and worthy of deeper study. He set himself the task of translating Diophantus's opus and publishing it so that the techniques of the Greeks could be re-kindled. It is important to realize that vast quantities of ancient mathematical knowledge had been completely forgotten. Higher mathematics was not taught in even the greatest European universities, and it is only thanks to the efforts of scholars such as Bachet that so much was revived so rapidly. In 1621 when Bachet published the Latin version of the *Arithmetica*, he was contributing to the second golden age of mathematics.

The *Arithmetica* contains over one hundred problems, and for each one Diophantus gives a detailed solution. This level of consci-entiousness was not a habit that Fermat ever picked up. Fermat was not interested in writing a textbook for future generations: He merely wanted to satisfy himself that he had solved a problem. While studying Diophantus's problems and solutions, he would be inspired to think of and tackle other related and more subtle questions. Fermat would scribble down whatever was necessary to convince himself that he could see the solution and then he would not bother to write down the remainder of the proof. More often than not he would consign his inspirational jottings to the bin, and then move on to the next problem. Fortunately for us, Bachet's publication of the *Arithmetica* contained generous margins on every page, and sometimes Fermat would hastily write logic and comments in these columns. These marginal notes would become an invaluable, if somewhat scanty, record of Fermat's most brilliant calculations.

One of Fermat's discoveries concerned the so-called *friendly numbers*, or *amicable numbers*, closely related to the perfect numbers that had fascinated Pythagoras two thousand years earlier. Friendly numbers are pairs of numbers such that each number is the sum of the divisors of the other number. The Pythagoreans made the extraordinary discovery that 220 and 284 are friendly numbers. The divisors of 220 are 1, 2, 4, 5, 10, 11, 20, 22, 44, 55, 110, and the sum of all these is 284. On the other hand, the divisors of 284 are 1, 2, 4, 71, 142, and the sum of all these is 220.

The pair 220 and 284 was said to be symbolic of friendship. Martin Gardner's book *Mathematical Magic Show* tells of talismans sold in the Middle Ages that were inscribed with these numbers on the grounds that wearing the charms would promote love. An Arab numerologist documents the practice of carving 220 on one fruit and 284 on another, and then eating the first one and offering the second one to a lover as a form of mathematical aphrodisiac. Early theologians noted that in Genesis Jacob gave 220 goats to Esau. They believed that the number of goats, one half of a friendly pair, was an expression of Jacob's love for Esau.

No other friendly numbers were identified until 1636, when

Fermat discovered the pair 17,296 and 18,416. Although not a profound discovery, it demonstrates Fermat's familiarity with numbers and his love of playing with them. Fermat started a fad for finding friendly numbers; Descartes discovered a third pair (9,363,584 and 9,437,056), and Leonhard Euler went on to list sixty-two amicable pairs. Curiously they had all overlooked a much smaller pair of friendly numbers. In 1866 a sixteen-year-old Italian, Nicolò Paganini, discovered the pair 1,184 and 1,210.

During the twentieth century mathematicians have extended the idea further and have searched for so-called "sociable" numbers, three or more numbers that form a closed loop. For example, in this loop of five numbers (12,496; 14,288; 15,472; 14,536; 14,264) the divisors of the first number add up to the second, the divisors of the second add up to the third, the divisors of the third add up to the fourth, the divisors of the fourth add up to the fifth, and the divisors of the fifth add up to the first.

Although discovering a new pair of friendly numbers made Fermat something of a celebrity, his reputation was truly confirmed thanks to a series of mathematical challenges. For example, Fermat noticed that 26 is sandwiched between 25 and 27, one of which is a square number ($25 = 5^2 = 5 \times 5$) and the other is a cube number ($27 = 3^3 = 3 \times 3 \times 3$). He searched for other numbers sandwiched between a square and a cube but failed to find any, and suspected that 26 might be unique. After days of strenuous effort he managed to construct an elaborate argument that proved without any doubt that 26 is indeed the only number between a square and a cube. His step-by-step logical proof established that no other numbers could fulfill this criterion.

Fermat announced this unique property of 26 to the mathematical community, and then challenged them to prove that this was the case. He openly admitted that he himself had a proof; the question was, however, did others have the ingenuity to match it? Despite the simplicity of the claim the proof is fiendishly complicated, and Fermat took particular delight in taunting the English mathematicians Wallis and Digby, who eventually had to admit defeat. Ultimately Fermat's greatest claim to fame would turn out to be another challenge to the rest of the world. However, it would be an accidental riddle that was never intended for public discussion.

The Marginal Note

While studying Book II of the *Arithmetica* Fermat came upon a whole series of observations, problems, and solutions that concerned Pythagoras's theorem and Pythagorean triples. Fermat was struck by the variety and sheer quantity of Pythagorean triples. He was aware that centuries earlier Euclid had stated a proof (outlined here in Appendix 5) which demonstrated that, in fact, there are an infinite number of Pythagorean triples. Fermat must have gazed at Diophantus's detailed exposition of Pythagorean triples and wondered what there was to add to the subject. As he stared at the page he began to play with Pythagoras's equation, trying to discover something that had evaded the Greeks.

Suddenly, in a moment of genius that would immortalize the Prince of Amateurs, he created an equation that, though very similar to Pythagoras's equation, had no solutions at all. This was the equation that the ten-year-old Andrew Wiles read about in the Milton Road Library.

Instead of considering the equation

$$x^2 + y^2 = z^2,$$

Fermat was contemplating a variant of Pythagoras's creation:

$$x^3 + y^3 = z^3.$$

As mentioned in the last chapter, Fermat had merely changed the power from 2 to 3, the square to a cube, but his new equation apparently had no whole number solutions whatsoever. Trial and error soon shows the difficulty of finding two cubed numbers that add together to make another cubed number. Could it really be the case that this minor modification turns Pythagoras's equation, one with an infinite number of solutions, into an equation with no solutions?

He altered the equation further by changing the power to numbers bigger than 3, and discovered that finding a solution to each of these equations was equally difficult. According to Fermat there appeared to be no three numbers that would perfectly fit the equation

$$x^n + y^n = z^n, \text{ where } n \text{ represents } 3, 4, 5, \dots$$

In the margin of his *Arithmetica*, next to Problem 8, he made a note of his observation:

Cubem autem in duos cubos, aut quadratoquadratum in duos quadratoquadratos, et generaliter nullam in infinitum ultra quadratum potestatem in duos eiusdem nominis fas est dividere.

It is impossible for a cube to be written as a sum of two cubes or a fourth power to be written as the sum of two fourth powers or, in general, for any number which is a power greater than the second to be written as a sum of two like powers.

Among all the possible numbers there seemed to be no reason why at least one set of solutions could not be found, yet Fermat stated that nowhere in the infinite universe of numbers was there a "Fermatean triple." It was an extraordinary claim, but one that Fermat believed he could prove. After the first marginal note outlining the theory, the mischievous genius jotted down an additional comment that would haunt generations of mathematicians:

> *Cuius rei demonstrationem mirabilem sane detexi hanc marginis exiguitas non caperet.*

> I have a truly marvelous demonstration of this proposition which this margin is too narrow to contain.

This was Fermat at his most infuriating. His own words suggest that he was particularly pleased with this "truly marvelous" proof, but he had no intention of bothering to write out the detail of the argument, never mind publishing it. He never told anyone about his proof, and yet, despite his combination of indolence and modesty, Fermat's Last Theorem, as it would later be called, would become famous around the world for centuries to come.

The Last Theorem Published at Last

Fermat's notorious discovery happened early in his mathematical career, in around 1637. Some thirty years later, while carrying out his judicial duties in the town of Castres, Fermat was taken seriously ill. On January 9, 1665, he signed his last *arrêt*, and three days later he died. Still isolated from the Parisian school of mathematics and not necessarily fondly remembered by his frustrated correspondents, Fermat's discoveries were at risk of being lost forever. Fortunately Fermat's eldest son, Clément-Samuel, who appreciated the significance of his father's hobby, was determined that his discoveries should not be lost to the world. It is thanks to his efforts that we know anything at all about Fermat's remarkable breakthroughs in number theory and, in particular, if it were not for Clément-Samuel, the enigma known as Fermat's Last Theorem would have died with its creator.

Clément-Samuel spent five years collecting his father's notes and letters, and examining the jottings in the margins of his copy of the *Arithmetica*. The marginal note referring to Fermat's Last Theorem was just one of many inspirational thoughts scribbled in the book, and Clément-Samuel undertook to publish these annotations in a special edition of the *Arithmetica*. In 1670 at Toulouse he brought out *Diophantus's Arithmetica Containing Observations by P. de Fermat*. Alongside Bachet's original Greek and Latin translations were forty-eight observations made by Fermat. The observation shown in Figure 6 was to be the one that would become known as Fermat's Last Theorem.

Once Fermat's *Observations* reached the wider community, it was clear that the letters he had sent to colleagues represented mere morsels from a treasure trove of discovery. His personal notes contained a whole series of theorems. Unfortunately these were accompanied either with no explanation at all or with only a slight hint of the underlying proof. There were just enough tantalizing glimpses of logic to leave mathematicians in no doubt that Fermat had proofs, but filling in the details was left as a challenge for them to take up.

Leonhard Euler, one of the greatest mathematicians of the eighteenth century, attempted to prove one of Fermat's most elegant observations, a theorem concerning prime numbers. A prime number is one that has no divisors — no number can be divided into it without a remainder, except for 1 and the number itself. For example, 13 is a prime number, but 14 is not. Nothing will divide into 13 perfectly, but 2 and 7 will divide into 14. All prime numbers can be put into two categories: those that equal $4n + 1$ and those that equal $4n - 1$, where n equals some number. So 13 is in the former group $(4 \times 3 + 1)$, whereas 19 is in the latter group $(4 \times 5 - 1)$. Fermat's prime theorem claimed that the first

DIOPHANTI

ALEXANDRINI
ARITHMETICORVM
LIBRI SEX,
ET DE NVMERIS MVLTANGVLIS
LIBER VNVS.

*CVM COMMENTARIIS C. G. BACHETI V. C.
& obseruationibus D. P. de FERMAT Senatoris Tolosani.*

Accessit Doctrinæ Analyticæ inuentum nouum, collectum
ex varijs eiusdem D. de FERMAT Epistolis.

TOLOSÆ,
Excudebat BERNARDVS BOSC, è Regione Collegij Societatis Iesu.

M. DC. LXX.

The frontispiece of Clément-Samuel Fermat's edition of
Diophantus's *Arithmetica*, published in 1670. This version
included the marginal notes made by his father.

interuallum numerorum 3. minor autem
1 N. atque ideo maior 1 N. + 2. Oportet
itaque 4 N. + 4. triplos esse ad 2. & ad-
huc superaddere 10. Ter igitur 2. adjici-
tis vnitatibus 10. æquatur 4 N. + 4. &
fit 1 N. 3. Erit ergo minor 3. maior 5. &
satisfaciunt quæstioni.

CONDITIONIS appositæ eadem ratio est quæ & appositæ præcedenti quæstioni, nil enim
aliud requirit quàm vt quadratus interualli numerorum sit minor interuallo quadratorum, &
Canones iidem hîc etiam locum habebunt, vt manifestum est.

QVÆSTIO VIII.

PROPOSITVM quadratum diuidere
in duos quadratos. Imperatum sit vt
16. diuidatur in duos quadratos. Ponatur
primus 1 Q. Oportet igitur 16 — 1 Q. æquales esse quadrato. Fingo quadratum a nume-
ris quotquot libuerit, cum defectu tot
vnitatum quod continet latus ipsius 16.
esto a 2 N. — 4. ipse igitur quadratus erit
4 Q. + 16. — 16 N. hæc æquabuntur vnitatibus 16 — 1 Q. Communis adiiciatur
vtrimque defectus, & a similibus auferan-
tur similia, fient 5 Q. æquales 16 N. & fit
1 N. ⁴⁄₅ Erit igitur alter quadratorum ¹⁴⁄₂₅.
alter vero ¹⁴⁄₂₅ & vtriusque summa est ⁴⁰⁰⁄₂₅ seu
16. & vterque quadratus est.

OBSERVATIO DOMINI PETRI DE FERMAT.

CVbum autem in duos cubos, aut quadratoquadratum in duos quadratoquadratos
& generaliter nullam in infinitum vltra quadratum potestatem in duos eiusdem
nominis fas est diuidere cuius rei demonstrationem mirabilem sane detexi.
Hanc marginis exiguitas non caperet.

QVÆSTIO IX.

RVRSVS oportet quadratum 16
diuidere in duos quadratos. Ponatur rursus primi latus 1 N. alterius verò quotcumque numerorum cum defectu tot vnitatum, quot constat latus diuidendi. Esto itaque 2 N. — 4. erunt quadrati, hic quidem 1 Q. ille verò 4 Q. + 16. — 16 N. Cæterum volo vtrumque simul æquari vnitatibus 16. Igitur 5 Q. + 16. — 16 N. æquatur vnitatibus 16. & fit 1 N. ⁴⁄₅ erit

H iij

type of primes were always the sum of two squares $(13 = 2^2 + 3^2)$, whereas the second type could never be written in this way. This property of primes is beautifully simple, but trying to prove that it is true for every single prime number turns out to be remarkably difficult. For Fermat it was just one of many private proofs. The challenge for Euler was to rediscover Fermat's proof. Eventually, in 1749, after seven years' work and almost a century after Fermat's death, Euler succeeded in proving this prime number theorem.

Fermat's panoply of theorems ranged from the fundamental to the simply amusing. Mathematicians rank the importance of theorems according to their impact on the rest of mathematics. First, a theorem is considered important if it has a universal truth, that is to say, if it applies to an entire group of numbers. In the case of the prime number theorem, it is true not for just some prime numbers, but for all prime numbers. Second, theorems should reveal some deeper underlying truth about the relationship between numbers. A theorem can be the springboard for generating a whole host of other theorems, even inspiring the development of whole new branches of mathematics. Finally, a theorem is important if it solves a problem in an area of research that previously was hindered for the lack of one logical link. Many mathematicians have cried themselves to sleep knowing that they could achieve a major result if only they could establish one missing link in their chain of logic.

Because mathematicians employ theorems as stepping-stones to other results, it was essential that every single one of Fermat's theorems be proved. Just because Fermat said he had a proof of a theorem it could not be accepted at face value. Before it could be used, each theorem had to be proved with ruthless rigor, otherwise the consequences could have been disastrous. For example, imagine that mathematicians had accepted one of Fermat's theorems. It would then be incorporated as a single element in a whole series of other larger proofs. In due course these larger proofs would be incorporated into even larger proofs, and so on. Ultimately hundreds of theorems could come to rely on the truth of the original unchecked theorem. However, what if Fermat had made a mistake and the unchecked theorem was in fact wrong? All these other theorems which incorporated it would also be flawed, and vast areas of mathematics would collapse. Theorems are the foundations of mathematics, because once their truth has been established other theorems can safely be built on top of them. Unsubstantiated ideas are infinitely less valuable and are referred to as conjectures. Any logic that relies on a conjecture is itself merely a conjecture.

Fermat said he had a proof for every one of his observations, so for him they were theorems. However, until the community at large could rediscover the individual proofs each one could only be considered a conjecture. In fact for the last 350 years Fermat's Last Theorem should more accurately have been referred to as Fermat's Last Conjecture.

As the centuries passed, all his other observations were proved one by one, but Fermat's Last Theorem stubbornly refused to give in. In fact, it is called the "Last" Theorem because it remains the last one of the observations to be proved. Three centuries of effort failed to find a proof, and this led to its notoriety as the most demanding riddle in mathematics. However, this acknowledged difficulty does not necessarily mean that Fermat's Last Theorem is an important theorem in the ways described earlier.

The fame of Fermat's Last Theorem comes solely from the

sheer difficulty of proving it. An extra sparkle is added by the fact that the Prince of Amateurs said that he could prove this theorem that has since baffled generations of professional mathematicians. Fermat's offhand comments in the margin of his copy of the *Arithmetica* were read as a challenge to the world. He had proved the Last Theorem; the question was, could any mathematician match his brilliance?

Fermat's Last Theorem is a problem of immense difficulty, and yet it can be stated in a form that a schoolchild can understand. There can be no problem in physics, chemistry, or biology that can be so simply and unambiguously stated and that has remained unsolved for so long. In *The Last Problem*, E. T. Bell wrote that civilization would probably come to an end before Fermat's Last Theorem could be solved. Proving Fermat's Last Theorem has become the most valuable prize in number theory, and not surprisingly it has led to some of the most exciting episodes in the history of mathematics.

The riddle's status has gone beyond the closed world of mathematics. In 1958 it even made its way into a Faustian tale. An anthology entitled *Deals with the Devil* contains a short story written by Arthur Porges. In "The Devil and Simon Flagg" the Devil asks Simon Flagg to set him a question. If the Devil succeeds in answering it within twenty-four hours then he takes Simon's soul, but if he fails then he must give Simon $100,000. Simon poses the question: "Is Fermat's Last Theorem correct?" The Devil disappears and whizzes around the world to absorb every piece of mathematics that has ever been created in order to prove the Last Theorem. The following day he returns and admits defeat:

> "You win, Simon," he said, almost in a whisper, eyeing him with ungrudging respect. "Not even I can learn enough mathematics in such a short time for so difficult a problem. The more I got into it

the worse it became. Non-unique factoring, ideals — Bah! Do you know," the Devil confided, "not even the best mathematicians on other planets — all far ahead of yours — have solved it? Why, there's a chap on Saturn — he looks something like a mushroom on stilts — who solves partial differential equations mentally; and even he's given up."

Leonhard Euler

3

A Mathematical Disgrace

Mathematics is not a careful march down a well-cleared highway, but a journey into a strange wilderness, where the explorers often get lost. Rigor should be a signal to the historian that the maps have been made, and the real explorers have gone elsewhere.

W. S. Anglin

"Since I first met Fermat's Last Theorem as a child it's been my greatest passion," recalls Andrew Wiles, in a hesitant voice that conveys the emotion he feels about the problem. "I'd found this problem that had been unsolved for three hundred years. I don't think many of my schoolfriends caught the mathematics bug, so I didn't discuss it with my contemporaries. But I did have a teacher who had done research in mathematics, and he gave me a book about number theory that gave me some clues about how to start tackling it. To begin with I worked on the assumption that Fermat didn't know very much more mathematics than I would have known. I tried to find his lost solution by using the kind of methods he might have used."

Wiles was a child full of innocence and ambition, who saw an opportunity to succeed where generations of mathematicians had failed. To others this might have seemed like a foolhardy dream, but young Wiles was right in thinking that he, a twentieth-century schoolboy, knew as much mathematics as Pierre de Fermat, a genius of the seventeenth century. Perhaps in his naïveté he would stumble upon a proof that other, more sophisticated minds had missed.

Despite his enthusiasm every calculation resulted in a dead end. Having racked his brains and sifted through his schoolbooks he was achieving nothing. After a year of failure he changed his strategy and decided that he might be able to learn something from the mistakes of other, more eminent mathematicians. "Fermat's Last Theorem has this incredible romantic history to it. Many people have thought about it, and the more that great mathematicians in the past have tried and failed to solve the problem, the more of a challenge and the more of a mystery it's become. Many mathematicians had tried it in so many different ways in the eighteenth and nineteenth centuries, and so as a teenager I decided that I ought to study those methods and try to understand what they'd been doing."

Young Wiles examined the approaches of everyone who had ever made a serious attempt to prove Fermat's Last Theorem. He began by studying the work of the most prolific mathematician in history and the first one to make a breakthrough in the battle against Fermat.

The Mathematical Cyclops

Creating mathematics is a painful and mysterious experience. Often the object of the proof is clear, but the route is shrouded in fog, and the mathematician stumbles through a calculation, terrified that each step might be taking the argument in completely the wrong direction. Additionally there is the fear that no route exists. A mathematician may believe that a statement is true, and spend years trying to prove that it is indeed true, when all along it is actually false. The mathematician has effectively been attempting to prove the impossible.

In the entire history of the subject only a handful of mathematicians appear to have avoided the self-doubt that intimidates their colleagues. Perhaps the most notable example of such a mathematician was the eighteenth-century genius Leonhard Euler, and it was he who made the first breakthrough toward proving Fermat's Last Theorem. Euler had such an incredible intuition and vast memory that it was said he could map out the entire bulk of a calculation in his head without having to put pen to paper. Across Europe he was referred to as "analysis incarnate," and the French academician François Arago said, "Euler calculated without apparent effort as men breathe, or as eagles sustain themselves in the wind."

Leonhard Euler was born in Basle in 1707, the son of a Calvinist pastor, Paul Euler. Although the young Euler showed a prodigious talent for mathematics, his father was determined that he should study theology and pursue a career in the Church. Leonhard dutifully obeyed and studied theology and Hebrew at the University of Basle.

Fortunately for Euler the town of Basle was also home to the eminent Bernoulli clan. The Bernoullis could easily claim to be the most mathematical of families, creating eight of Europe's most outstanding minds within only three generations — some have said that the Bernoulli family was to mathematics what the Bach family was to music. Their fame spread beyond the mathematical community, and one particular legend typifies the profile of the family. Daniel Bernoulli was once traveling across Europe and had struck up a conversation with a stranger. After a while he modestly introduced himself: "I am Daniel Bernoulli." "And I," said his companion sarcastically, "am Isaac Newton." Daniel fondly recalled this incident on several occasions, considering it the most sincere tribute he had ever received.

Daniel and Nikolaus Bernoulli were close friends of Leonhard Euler, and they realized that the most brilliant of mathematicians was being turned into the most mediocre of theologians. They appealed to Paul Euler and requested that Leonhard be allowed to forsake the cloth in favor of numbers. Euler senior had in the past been taught mathematics by Bernoulli senior, Jakob, and had a tremendous respect for the family. Reluctantly he accepted that his son had been born to calculate, not preach.

Leonhard Euler soon left Switzerland for the palaces of Berlin and St. Petersburg, where he was to spend the bulk of his creative years. During the era of Fermat, mathematicians were considered amateur number-jugglers, but by the eighteenth century they were treated as professional problem-solvers. The culture of numbers had changed dramatically, and this was partly a consequence of Sir Isaac Newton and his scientific calculations.

Newton believed that mathematicians were wasting their time teasing each other with pointless riddles. Instead he would apply mathematics to the physical world and calculate everything from the orbits of the planets to the trajectories of cannonballs. By the time Newton died, in 1727, Europe had undergone a scientific revolution, and in the same year Euler published his first paper. Although the paper contained elegant and innovative mathematics, it was primarily aimed at describing a solution to a technical problem regarding the masting of ships.

The European powers were not interested in using mathematics to explore esoteric and abstract concepts; instead they wanted to exploit mathematics to solve practical problems, and they competed to employ the best minds. Euler began his career with the Czars, before being invited to the Berlin Academy by Frederick the Great of Prussia. Eventually he returned to Russia, under the rule of Catherine the Great, where he spent his final years. During his career he tackled a multitude of problems, ranging from navigation to finance, and from acoustics to irrigation. However, the practical world of problem-solving did not dull Euler's mathematical ability. Instead tackling each new task would inspire him to create innovative and ingenious mathematics. His single-minded passion drove him to write several papers in a single day, and it is said that between the first and second calls for dinner he would attempt to dash off a complete calculation worthy of publication. Not a moment was wasted, and even when he was cradling an infant in one hand Euler would be outlining a proof with the other.

One of Euler's greatest achievements was the development of the algorithmic method. The point of Euler's algorithms was to tackle apparently impossible problems. One such problem was predicting the phases of the moon far into the future with high accuracy — information that could be used to draw up vital navigation tables. Newton had already shown that it is relatively easy to predict the orbit of one body around another, but in the case of the moon the situation is not so simple. The moon orbits the earth, but there is a third body, the sun, that complicates matters enormously. While the earth and moon attract each other, the sun perturbs the position of the earth and has a knock-on effect on the orbit of the moon. Equations could be used to pin down the effect of any two of the bodies, but eighteenth-century mathematicians could not incorporate the third body into their calculations. Even today it is impossible to predict the exact solution to the so-called "three-body problem."

Euler realized that mariners did not need to know the phase of the moon with absolute accuracy, only with enough precision to locate their own position to within a few nautical miles. Consequently Euler developed a recipe for generating an imperfect but sufficiently accurate solution. The recipe, known as an algorithm, worked by first obtaining a rough-and-ready result, which could then be fed back into the algorithm to generate a more refined result. This refined result could then be fed back into the algorithm to generate an even more accurate result, and so on. A hundred or so iterations later, Euler was able to provide a position for the moon that was accurate enough for the purposes of the navy. He gave his algorithm to the British Admiralty, and in return they rewarded him with a prize of £300.

Euler earned a reputation for being able to solve any problem that was posed, a talent that seemed to extend even beyond the realm of science. During his stint at the court of Catherine the Great he encountered the great French philosopher Denis Diderot. Diderot was a committed atheist and would spend his days converting the Russians to atheism. This infuriated Catherine, who asked Euler to put a stop to the efforts of the godless Frenchman.

Euler gave the matter some thought and claimed that he had an algebraic proof for the existence of God. Catherine the Great invited Euler and Diderot to the palace and gathered together her courtiers to listen to the theological debate. Euler stood before the audience and announced:

$$\text{``Sir, } \frac{a + b^n}{n} = x, \text{ hence God exists; reply!''}$$

With no great understanding of algebra, Diderot was unable to argue against the greatest mathematician in Europe and was

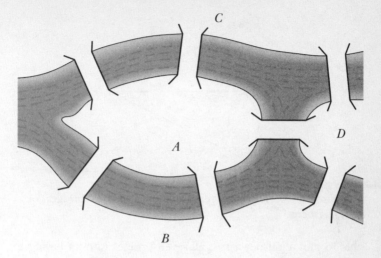

Figure 7. The river Pregel divides the town of Königsberg into four separate parts, *A*, *B*, *C* and *D*. Seven bridges connect the various parts of the town, and a local riddle asked if it was possible to make a journey such that each bridge is crossed once, and only once.

left speechless. Humiliated, he left St. Petersburg and returned to Paris. In his absence, Euler continued to enjoy his return to theological study and published several other mock proofs concerning the nature of God and the human spirit.

A more valid problem that also appealed to Euler's whimsical nature concerned the Prussian city of Königsberg, now known as the Russian city of Kaliningrad. The city is built on the banks of the river Pregel and consists of four separate quarters connected by seven bridges. Figure 7 shows the layout of the city. Some of the more curious residents of Königsberg wondered if it was pos-

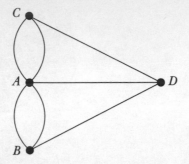

Figure 8. A simplified representation of the bridges of Königsberg.

sible to plot a journey across all seven bridges without having to stroll across any bridge more than once. The citizens of Königsberg tried various routes, but each one ended in failure. Euler also failed to find a successful route, but he was successful in explaining why making such a journey was impossible.

Euler began with a plan of the city, and from it he generated a simplified representation in which the sections of land were reduced to points and bridges were replaced by lines, as shown in Figure 8. He then argued that, in general, in order to make a successful journey (i.e., crossing all bridges only once) a point should be connected to an even number of lines. This is because in the middle of a journey when the traveler passes through a landmass, he or she must enter via one bridge and then leave via a different bridge. There are only two exceptions to this rule — when a traveler either begins or ends the journey. At the start of the journey the traveler leaves a landmass and requires only a single bridge to exit, and at the end of the journey the traveler arrives at a landmass and requires only a single bridge to enter. If the journey begins and ends in different locations, then these two landmasses are allowed to have an odd number of bridges. But if the journey begins and ends in the same place, then this point, like all the other points, must have an even number of bridges.

So, in general, Euler concluded that, for any network of bridges, it is only possible to make a complete journey crossing each bridge only once if all the landmasses have an even number of bridges, or exactly two landmasses have an odd number of bridges. In the case of Königsberg there are four landmasses in total and all of them are connected to an odd number of bridges — three points have three bridges, and one has five bridges. Euler had been able to explain why it was impossible to cross each one of Königsberg's bridges once and only once, and furthermore he had generated a rule that could be applied to any network of bridges in any city in the world. The argument is beautifully simple, and was perhaps just the sort of logical problem that Euler dashed off before dinner.

When Euler first encountered Fermat's Last Theorem, it must have looked about as simple as the Königsberg bridge problem, and he must have hoped that he would solve it by adapting an equally straightforward strategy. Recall that Fermat stated that there are no whole number solutions to the following equation:

$$x^n + y^n = z^n, \text{ where } n \text{ is any number greater than 2.}$$

This equation represents an infinite set of equations:

$$x^3 + y^3 = z^3,$$
$$x^4 + y^4 = z^4,$$
$$x^5 + y^5 = z^5,$$
$$x^6 + y^6 = z^6,$$
$$x^7 + y^7 = z^7,$$
$$\vdots$$

Euler wondered if he could prove that one of the equations had no solutions and then extrapolate the result to all the remaining equations.

His task was given a head start when he discovered a clue hidden in Fermat's jottings. Although Fermat never wrote down a proof for the Last Theorem, he did cryptically describe a proof for the specific case $n = 4$ elsewhere in his copy of the *Arithmetica* and incorporated it into the proof of a totally different problem. Even though this is the most complete calculation he ever committed to paper, the details are still sketchy and vague, and Fermat concludes the proof by saying that lack of time and paper prevent him from giving a fuller explanation. Despite the lack of detail in Fermat's scribbles, they clearly illustrate a particular form of proof by contradiction known as the *method of infinite descent*.

In order to prove that there were no solutions to the equation $x^4 + y^4 = z^4$, Fermat began by assuming that there was a hypothetical solution

$$x = X_1, \ y = Y_1, \ z = Z_1.$$

By examining the properties of (X_1, Y_1, Z_1), Fermat could demonstrate that if this hypothetical solution did exist then there would have to be a smaller solution (X_2, Y_2, Z_2). Then, by examining this new solution, Fermat could show there would be an even smaller solution (X_3, Y_3, Z_3), and so on.

Fermat had discovered a descending staircase of solutions, which theoretically would continue forever, generating ever-smaller numbers. However, x, y, and z must be whole numbers, and so the never-ending staircase is impossible because there must be a smallest possible solution. This contradiction proves that the initial assumption, that there is a solution (X_1, Y_1, Z_1), must be false. Using the method of infinite descent, Fermat had demonstrated that it is forbidden for the equation with $n = 4$ to have any solutions, because if it did the consequences would be illogical.

Euler tried to use this as a starting point for constructing a general proof for all the other equations. As well as building up to $n =$ infinity, he would also have to build down to $n = 3$, and it was this single downward step that he attempted first. On August 4, 1753, Euler announced in a letter to the Prussian mathematician Christian Goldbach that he had adapted Fermat's method of infinite descent and successfully proved the case for $n = 3$. After a hundred years this was the first time anybody had succeeded in making any progress toward meeting Fermat's challenge.

In order to extend Fermat's proof from $n = 4$ to cover the case $n = 3$ Euler had to incorporate the bizarre concept of a so-called *imaginary number*, an entity that had been discovered by European mathematicians in the sixteenth century. It is strange to think of new numbers being "discovered," but this is mainly because we are so familiar with the numbers we commonly use that we forget that there was a time when some of these numbers were not known. Negative numbers, fractions, and irrational numbers all had to be discovered, and the motivation in each case was to answer otherwise unanswerable questions.

The history of numbers begins with the simple counting numbers (1, 2, 3, …) otherwise known as natural numbers. These numbers are perfectly satisfactory for adding together simple whole quantities, such as sheep or gold coins, to achieve a total number that is also a whole quantity. As well as addition, the other simple operation of multiplication also acts upon whole numbers to generate other whole numbers. However, the operation of division throws up an awkward problem. While 8 divided by 2 equals 4, we find that 2 divided by 8 equals $\frac{1}{4}$. The result of the latter division is not a whole number but a fraction.

Division is a simple operation performed on natural numbers that requires us to look beyond the natural numbers in order to obtain the answer. It is unthinkable for mathematicians not, in theory at least, to be able to answer every single question, and this necessity is called *completeness*. There are certain questions concerning natural numbers that would be unanswerable without resorting to fractions. Mathematicians express this by saying that fractions are necessary for completeness.

It is this need for completeness that led the Hindus to discover negative numbers. The Hindus noticed that, while 3 subtracted from 5 was obviously 2, subtracting 5 from 3 was not such a simple matter. The answer was beyond the natural counting numbers, and could only be accommodated by introducing the concept of negative numbers. Some mathematicians did not accept this extension into abstraction and referred to negative numbers as "absurd" or "fictitious." While an accountant could hold one gold coin, or even half a gold coin, it was impossible to hold a negative coin.

The Greeks also had a yearning for completeness, and this led them to discover irrational numbers. In Chapter 2 the question arose, *What number is the square root of two, $\sqrt{2}$?* The Greeks knew that this number was roughly equal to $\frac{7}{5}$, but when they tried to discover the exact fraction they found that it did not exist. Here was a number that could never be represented as a fraction, but this new type of number was necessary in order to answer a simple question, *What is the square root of two?* The demand for completeness meant that yet another colony was added to the empire of numbers.

By the Renaissance, mathematicians assumed that they had discovered all the numbers in the universe. All numbers could

Figure 9. All numbers can be positioned along the number line, which extends to infinity in both directions.

be thought of as lying on a *number line*—an infinitely long line with zero at the center, as shown in Figure 9. The whole numbers were spaced equally along the number line, with the positive numbers on the right of zero extending to positive infinity and the negative numbers on the left of zero extending to negative infinity. The fractions occupied the spaces between the whole numbers, and the irrational numbers were interspersed between the fractions.

The number line suggested that completeness had apparently been achieved. All the numbers seemed to be in place, ready to answer all mathematical questions — in any case, there was no more room on the number line for any new numbers. Then during the sixteenth century there were renewed rumblings of disquiet. The Italian mathematician Rafaello Bombelli was studying the square roots of various numbers when he stumbled upon an unanswerable question.

The problem began by asking, *What is the square root of one, $\sqrt{1}$?* The obvious answer is 1, because $1 \times 1 = 1$. The less obvious answer is -1. A negative number multiplied by another negative number generates a positive number. This means $-1 \times -1 = +1$. So, the square root of $+1$ is both $+1$ and -1. This abundance of answers is fine, but then the question arises, *What is the square root of negative one, $\sqrt{-1}$?* The problem seems to be intractable. The solution cannot be $+1$ or -1, because the square of both these numbers is +1. However, there are no other obvious candidates. At the same time completeness demands that we must be able to answer the question.

The solution for Bombelli was to create a new number, i, called an *imaginary number*, which was simply defined as the solution to the question, *What is the square root of negative one?* This might seem like a cowardly solution to the problem, but it was no different to the way in which negative numbers were introduced. Faced with an otherwise unanswerable question, the Hindus merely defined −1 as the solution to the question, *What is zero subtract one?* It is easier to accept the concept of −1 only because we have experience of the analogous concept of "debt," whereas we have nothing in the real world to underpin the concept of an imaginary number. The seventeenth-century German mathematician Gottfried Leibniz elegantly described the strange nature of the imaginary number: "The imaginary number is a fine and wonderful recourse of the divine spirit, almost an amphibian between being and non-being."

Once we have defined i as being the square root of −1, then $2i$ must exist, because this would be the sum of i plus i (as well as being the square root of −4). Similarly, $\frac{i}{2}$ must exist because this is the result of dividing i by 2. By performing simple operations it is possible to achieve an imaginary equivalent of every so-called *real number.* There are imaginary counting numbers, imaginary negative numbers, imaginary fractions, and imaginary irrationals.

The problem that now arises is that all these imaginary numbers have no natural position along the real number line. Mathematicians resolve this crisis by creating a separate imaginary number line that is perpendicular to the real one, and that crosses at zero, as shown in Figure 10. Numbers are now no longer restricted to a one-dimensional line, but rather they oc-

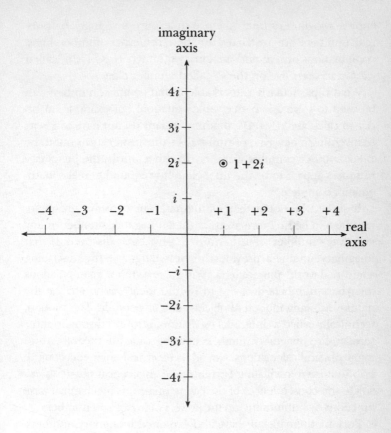

Figure 10. The introduction of an axis for imaginary numbers turns the number line into a number plane. Any combination of real and imaginary numbers has a position on the number plane.

cupy a two-dimensional plane. While pure imaginary or pure real numbers are restricted to their respective number lines, combinations of real and imaginary numbers (e.g., 1+2i), called *complex numbers*, live on the so-called number plane.

What is particularly remarkable is that complex numbers can be used to solve any conceivable equation. For example, in order to calculate $\sqrt{(3 + 4i)}$, mathematicians do not have to resort to inventing a new type of number — the answer turns out to be $2 + i$, another complex number. In other words, the imaginary numbers appear to be the final element required to make mathematics complete.

It should be noted that mathematicians consider imaginary numbers to be no more abstract than a negative number or any counting number. Furthermore, physicists discovered that imaginary numbers provide the best language for describing some real-world phenomena. With a few minor manipulations imaginary numbers turn out to be the ideal way to analyze the natural swinging motion of objects such as pendula. This motion, technically called a sinusoidal oscillation, is found throughout nature, and so imaginary numbers have become an integral part of many physical calculations. Nowadays electrical engineers conjure up i to analyze oscillating currents, and theoretical physicists calculate the consequences of oscillating quantum mechanical wave functions by summoning up the powers of imaginary numbers.

Pure mathematicians have also exploited imaginary numbers, using them to find answers to previously impenetrable problems. Imaginary numbers literally add a new dimension to mathematics, and Euler hoped to exploit this extra degree of freedom to attack Fermat's Last Theorem.

In the past other mathematicians had tried to adapt Fermat's method of infinite descent to work for cases other than $n = 4$, but in every case attempts to stretch the proof only led to gaps in the logic. However, Euler showed that by incorporating the imaginary number, i, into his proof he could plug holes in the proof and force the method of infinite descent to work for the case $n = 3$.

It was a tremendous achievement, but one that he could not repeat for other cases of Fermat's Last Theorem. Unfortunately Euler's endeavors to make the argument work for the cases up to infinity all ended in failure. The man who created more mathematics than anybody else in history was humbled by Fermat's challenge. His only consolation was that he had made the first breakthrough in the world's hardest problem.

Euler continued to create brilliant mathematics until the day he died, an achievement made all the more remarkable by the fact that during the final years of his career he was totally blind. His loss of sight began in 1735 when the Academy in Paris offered a prize for the solution to an astronomical problem. The problem was so awkward that the mathematical community asked the Academy to allow them several months in which to come up with an answer, but for Euler this was unnecessary. He became obsessed with the task, worked continually for three days, and duly won the prize. However, poor working conditions combined with intense stress cost Euler, then still only in his twenties, the sight of one eye. This is apparent in many portraits of Euler, including the one at the front of this chapter.

On the advice of Jean Le Rond d'Alembert, Euler was replaced by Joseph-Louis Lagrange as mathematician to the court of Frederick the Great, who later commented: "To your care and recommendation am I indebted for having replaced a half-blind mathematician with a mathematician with both eyes, which will especially please the anatomical members of my Academy." Euler returned to Russia, where Catherine the

Great welcomed back her "mathematical cyclops."

The loss of one eye was only a minor handicap — in fact Euler claimed that "now I will have less distraction." Forty years later, at the age of sixty, his situation worsened considerably, when a cataract in Euler's good eye meant he was destined to become completely blind. He was determined not to give in and began to practice writing with his fading eye closed in order to perfect his technique before the onset of darkness. Within weeks he was blind.

Euler continued to produce mathematics for the next seventeen years, and, if anything, he was more productive than ever. His immense intellect allowed him to juggle concepts without having to commit them to paper, and his phenomenal memory allowed him to use his own brain as a mental library. Colleagues suggested that the onset of blindness appeared to expand the horizons of his imagination. It is worth noting that Euler's computations of lunar positions were completed during his period of blindness. For the emperors of Europe this was the most prized of mathematical achievements, a problem that had confounded the greatest mathematicians in Europe, including Newton.

In 1776 an operation was performed to remove the cataract, and for a few days Euler's sight seemed to have been restored. Then infection set in and Euler was plunged back into darkness. Undaunted, he continued to work until, on September 18, 1783, he suffered a fatal stroke. In the words of the mathematician-philosopher the Marquis de Condorcet, "Euler ceased to live and calculate."

A Petty Pace

A century after Fermat's death there existed proofs for only two specific cases of the Last Theorem. Fermat had given mathematicians a head start by providing them with the proof that there were no solutions to the equation

$$x^4 + y^4 = z^4.$$

Euler had adapted the proof to show that there were no solutions to

$$x^3 + y^3 = z^3.$$

After Euler's breakthrough it was still necessary to prove that there were no whole number solutions to an infinity of other equations:

$$x^5 + y^5 = z^5,$$
$$x^6 + y^6 = z^6,$$
$$x^7 + y^7 = z^7,$$
$$x^8 + y^8 = z^8,$$
$$\vdots$$

Although mathematicians were making embarrassingly slow progress, the situation was not quite as bad as it might seem at first sight. The proof for the case $n = 4$ also proves the cases $n = 8, 12, 16, 20, \dots$. The reason is that any number that can be written as an 8th (or a 12th, 16th, 20th, ...) power can also be rewritten as a 4th power. For instance, the number 256 is equal to 2^8, but it is also equal to 4^4. Therefore any proof that works for the 4th power will also work for the 8th power and for any other power that is a multiple of 4. Using the same principle, Euler's proof for the case $n = 3$ automatically proves the cases $n = 6, 9, 12, 15, \dots$

Suddenly, the numbers are tumbling and Fermat looks vulnerable. The proof for the case $n = 3$ is particularly significant because the number 3 is an example of a *prime number*. As explained earlier, a prime number has the special property of not being the multiple of any whole number except for 1 and itself. Other prime numbers are 5, 7, 11, 13, ... All the remaining numbers are multiples of the primes, and are referred to as non-primes, or composite numbers.

Number theorists consider prime numbers to be the most important numbers of all, because they are the atoms of mathematics. Prime numbers are the numerical building blocks, because all other numbers can be created by multiplying combinations of the prime numbers. This seems to lead to a remarkable breakthrough. To prove Fermat's Last Theorem for all values of n, one merely has to prove it for the prime values of n. All other cases are merely multiples of the prime cases and would be proved implicitly.

Intuitively this enormously simplifies the problem, because you can ignore those equations that involve a value of n that is not a prime number. The number of equations remaining is now vastly reduced. For example, for the values of n up to 20, there are only six values that need to be proved:

$$x^5 + y^5 = z^5,$$
$$x^7 + y^7 = z^7,$$
$$x^{11} + y^{11} = z^{11},$$
$$x^{13} + y^{13} = z^{13},$$
$$x^{17} + y^{17} = z^{17},$$
$$x^{19} + y^{19} = z^{19}.$$

If one can prove Fermat's Last Theorem for just the prime values of n, then the theorem is proved for all values of n. If one considers all whole numbers, then it is obvious that there are infinitely many. If one considers just the prime numbers, which are only a small fraction of all the whole numbers, then surely the problem is much simpler?

Intuition would suggest that if you begin with an infinite quantity and then remove the bulk of it, then you would expect to be left with something finite. Unfortunately intuition is not the arbiter of truth in mathematics, but rather logic. In fact, it is possible to prove that the list of primes is never-ending. Therefore, despite being able to ignore the vast majority of equations relating to non-prime values of n, the remaining equations relating to prime values of n are still infinite in number.

The proof that there is an infinity of primes dates all the way back to Euclid, and is one of the classic arguments of mathematics. Initially Euclid assumes that there is a finite list of known prime numbers, and then shows that there must exist an infinite number of additions to this list. There are N prime numbers in Euclid's finite list, which are labeled $P_1, P_2, P_3, ..., P_N$. Euclid can then generate a new number Q_A such that

$$Q_A = (P_1 \times P_2 \times P_3 \times ... \times P_N) + 1.$$

This new number Q_A is either prime or not prime. If it is prime then we have succeeded in generating a new, bigger prime number, and therefore our original list of primes was not complete. On the other hand, if Q_A is not prime, then it must be perfectly divisible by a prime. This prime cannot be one of the known primes because dividing Q_A by any of the known primes will inevitably lead to a remainder of 1. Therefore there must be some new prime, which we can call P_{N+1}.

We have now arrived at the stage where either Q_A is a new prime or we have another new prime P_{N+1}. Either way we have added to our original list of primes. We can now repeat the process, including our new prime (P_{N+1} or Q_A) in our list, and generate some new number Q_B. Either this new number will be yet another new prime, or there will have to be some other new prime P_{N+2}, which is not on our list of known primes. The upshot of the argument is that, however long our list of prime numbers, it is always possible to find a new one. Therefore the list of primes is never-ending and infinite.

But how can something that is undeniably smaller than an infinite quantity also be infinite? At the beginning of the twentieth century the German mathematician David Hilbert said: "The infinite! No other question has ever moved so profoundly the spirit of man; no other idea has so fruitfully stimulated his intellect; yet no other concept stands in greater need of clarification than that of the infinite."

To help explain the mystery of infinity, Hilbert created an example of infinity, known as *Hilbert's Hotel.* This hypothetical hotel has the desirable attribute of having an infinite number of rooms. One day a new guest arrives and is disappointed to learn that, despite the hotel's infinite size, all the rooms are occupied. Hilbert, the clerk, thinks for a while and then reassures the new arrival that he will find an empty room. He asks all his current guests to move to the next room, so that the guest in room 1 moves to room 2, the guest in room 2 moves to room 3, and so on. Everybody who was in the hotel still has a room, which allows the new arrival to slip into the vacant room 1. This shows that infinity plus one equals infinity. Similarly, infinity subtract one is still infinity, and indeed infinity subtract one million is still infinity.

The following night Hilbert has to deal with a much greater problem. The hotel is still full when an infinitely large coach arrives with an infinite number of new guests. Hilbert remains unperturbed and rubs his hands at the thought of infinitely more hotel bills. He asks all his current guests to move to the room that is double the number of their current room. So the guest in room 1 moves to room 2, the guest in room 2 moves to room 4, and so on. Everybody who was in the hotel still has a room and yet an infinite number of rooms, all the odd ones, have been vacated for the new arrivals. This shows that double infinity is still infinity. And half of infinity is still infinity.

Hilbert's Hotel seems to suggest that all infinities are as large as each other, because various infinities seem to be able to squeeze into the same infinite hotel — the infinity of even numbers can be matched up and compared with the infinity of all counting numbers. However, some infinities are indeed bigger than others. For example, any attempt to pair every rational number with every irrational number ends in failure, and in fact it can be proved that the infinite set of irrational numbers is larger than the infinite set of rational numbers. Mathematicians have had to develop a whole system of nomenclature to deal with the varying scales of infinity, and conjuring with these concepts is one of today's hottest topics.

Although the infinity of primes dashed hopes for an early proof of Fermat's Last Theorem, a countless supply of prime numbers does have more positive implications in other areas, such as espionage and the evolution of insects. Before returning to the quest for a proof of Fermat's Last Theorem it is worth briefly investigating the uses and abuses of primes.

Prime number theory is one of the few areas of pure mathematics that has found a direct application in the real world, namely in cryptography. Cryptography involves scrambling secret messages so that they can only be unscrambled by the receiver and not by anybody else who might intercept them. The scrambling process requires the use of a secret key, and traditionally unscrambling the message simply requires the receiver to apply the key in reverse. With this procedure the key is the weakest link in the chain of security. First, the receiver and the sender must agree on the details of the key, and the exchange of this information is a risky process. If the enemy can intercept the key being exchanged, then they can unscramble all subsequent messages. Second, the keys must be regularly changed in order to maintain security, and each time this happens there is a risk of the new key being intercepted.

The problem of the key revolves around the fact that applying it one way will scramble the message, and applying it in reverse unscrambles the message — unscrambling a message is almost as easy as scrambling it. However, experience tells us that there are many everyday situations when unscrambling is far harder than scrambling — it is relatively easy to scramble an egg, but to unscramble it is far harder.

In the 1970s Whitfield Diffie and Martin Hellman came up with the idea of looking for a mathematical process that was easy to perform in one direction but incredibly difficult to perform in the opposite direction. Such a process would provide a perfect key. For example, I could have my own two-part key, and publish the scrambling half of it in a public directory. Then anybody could send me scrambled messages, but only I would know the unscrambling half of the key. Although everyone would have knowledge of the scrambling part of the key, it bears no relation to the unscrambling part of the key.

In 1977 Ronald Rivest, Adi Shamir, and Leonard Adleman, a team of mathematicians and computer scientists at the Massachusetts Institute of Technology, realized that prime numbers were the ideal basis for an easy-scramble/hard-unscramble process. In order to make my own personal key I would take two huge prime numbers, each one containing up to 80 digits, and then multiply them together to achieve an even larger nonprime number. In order to scramble messages all that is required is knowledge of the large non-prime number, whereas to unscramble the message you would need to know the two original prime numbers that were multiplied together, known as the prime factors. I can now publish the large non-prime number, the scrambling half of the key, and keep the two prime factors, the unscrambling half of the key, to myself. Importantly, even though everybody knows the large non-prime number, they would have immense difficulty in working out the two prime factors.

Taking a simpler example, I could hand out the non-prime number 589, which would enable everyone to scramble messages to me. I would keep the two prime factors of 589 secret, so that only I could unscramble the messages. If others could work out the two prime factors then they too could unscramble my messages, but even with this small number it is not obvious what the two prime factors are. In this case it would take only a few minutes on a personal computer to figure out that the prime factors are actually 31 and 19 ($31 \times 19 = 589$), and so my key would not remain secure for very long.

However, in reality the non-prime number that I would publish would have over a hundred digits, which makes the task of finding its prime factors effectively impossible. Even if the world's most powerful computers were used to split this huge non-prime number (the scrambling key) into its two prime factors (the unscrambling key) it would take several years to achieve the answer. Therefore, to foil foreign spies, I merely have to change my key on an annual basis. Once a year I announce my new giant non-prime number, and anybody who wants to try to unscramble my messages would then have to start all over again trying to compute the two prime factors.

As well as finding a role in espionage, prime numbers also appear in the natural world. The periodical cicadas, most notably *Magicicada septendecim*, have the longest life cycle of any insect. Their unique life cycle begins underground, where the nymphs patiently suck the juice from the roots of trees. Then, after 17 years of waiting, the adult cicadas emerge from the ground, swarm in vast numbers, and temporarily swamp the landscape. Within a few weeks they mate, lay their eggs, and die.

The question that puzzled biologists was, *Why is the cicada's life cycle so long?* And is there any significance to the life cycle being a prime number of years? Another species, *Magicicada tredecim*, swarms every 13 years, implying that life cycles lasting a prime number of years offer some evolutionary advantage.

One theory suggests that the cicada has a parasite that also goes through a lengthy life cycle and that the cicada is trying to avoid. If the parasite has a life cycle of, say, 2 years then the cicada wants to avoid a life cycle that is divisible by 2, otherwise the parasite and the cicada will regularly coincide. Similarly, if the parasite has a life cycle of 3 years then the cicada wants to avoid a life cycle that is divisible by 3, otherwise the parasite and the cicada will once again regularly coincide. Ultimately, to avoid meeting its parasite the cicadas' best strategy is to have a long life cycle lasting a prime number of years. Because nothing will divide into 17, *Magicicada septendecim* will rarely meet its parasite. If the parasite has a 2-year life cycle they will meet only every 34 years, and if it has a longer life cycle, say 16 years, then they will meet only every 272 (16×17) years.

In order to fight back, the parasite has only two life cycles that will increase the frequency of coincidences — the annual cycle and the same 17-year cycle as the cicada. However, the parasite is unlikely to survive reappearing 17 years in a row, because for the first 16 appearances there will be no cicadas for it to parasitize. On the other hand, in order to reach the 17-year life cycle, the generations of parasites would first have to evolve through the 16-year life cycle. This would mean at some stage of evolution the parasite and cicada would not coincide for 272 years! In either case the cicada's long prime life cycle protects it.

This might explain why the alleged parasite has never been found! In the race to keep up with the cicada, the parasite probably kept extending its life cycle until it hit the 16-year hurdle. Then it failed to coincide for 272 years, by which time the lack of coinciding with cicadas had driven it to extinction. The result is a cicada with a 17-year life cycle, which it no longer needs because its parasite no longer exists.

Monsieur Le Blanc

By the beginning of the nineteenth century, Fermat's Last Theorem had already established itself as the most notorious problem in number theory. Since Euler's breakthrough there had been no further progress, but a dramatic announcement by a young Frenchwoman was to reinvigorate the pursuit of Fermat's lost proof. Sophie Germain lived in an era of chauvinism and prejudice, and in order to conduct her research she was forced to assume a false identity, study in terrible conditions, and work in intellectual isolation.

Over the centuries women have been discouraged from studying mathematics, but despite the discrimination there have been several female mathematicians who fought against the establishment and indelibly forged their names in the annals of mathematics. The first woman known to have made an impact on the subject was Theano in the sixth century B.C., who began

Sophie Germain

as one of Pythagoras's students before becoming one of his foremost disciples and eventually marrying him. Pythagoras is known as the "feminist philosopher" because he actively encouraged women scholars, Theano being just one of the twenty-eight sisters in the Pythagorean Brotherhood.

In later centuries the likes of Socrates and Plato would continue to invite women into their schools, but it was not until the fourth century A.D. that a woman mathematician founded her own influential school. Hypatia, the daughter of a mathematics teacher at the University of Alexandria, was famous for giving the most popular discourses in the known world and for being the greatest of problem-solvers. Mathematicians who had been stuck for months on a particular problem would write to her seeking a solution, and Hypatia rarely disappointed her admirers. She was obsessed by mathematics and the process of logical proof, and when asked why she never married she replied that she was wedded to the truth. Ultimately her devotion to the cause of rationalism caused her downfall, when Cyril, the patriarch of Alexandria, began to oppress philosophers, scientists, and mathematicians, whom he called heretics. The historian Edward Gibbon provided a vivid account of what happened after Cyril had plotted against Hypatia and turned the masses against her:

> On a fatal day, in the holy season of Lent, Hypatia was torn from her chariot, stripped naked, dragged to the church, and inhumanely butchered by the hands of Peter the Reader and a troop of savage and merciless fanatics; her flesh was scraped from her bones with sharp oyster-shells, and her quivering limbs were delivered to the flames.

Soon after the death of Hypatia mathematics entered a period of stagnation, and it was not until after the Renaissance that another woman made her name as a mathematician. Maria Agnesi was born in Milan in 1718 and, like Hypatia, was the daughter of a mathematician. She was acknowledged to be one of the finest mathematicians in Europe, particularly famous for her treatises on the tangents to curves. In Italian, curves were called *versiera*, a word derived from the Latin *vertere*, "to turn," but it was also an abbreviation for *avversiera*, or "wife of the Devil." A curve studied by Agnesi *(versiera Agnesi)* was mistranslated into English as the "witch of Agnesi," and in time the mathematician herself was referred to by the same title.

Although mathematicians across Europe acknowledged Agnesi's ability, many academic institutions, in particular the French Academy, refused to give her a research post. Institutionalized discrimination against women continued right through to the twentieth century, when Emmy Noether, described by Einstein as "the most significant creative mathematical genius thus far produced since the higher education of women began," was denied a lectureship at the University of Göttingen. The majority of the faculty argued: "How can it be allowed that a woman become a *Privatdozent*? Having become a *Privatdozent*, she can then become a professor and a member of the University Senate . . . . What will our soldiers think when they return to the University and find that they are expected to learn at the feet of a woman?" Her friend and mentor David Hilbert replied: "Meine Herren, I do not see that the sex of the candidate is an argument against her admission as a *Privatdozent*. After all, the Senate is not a bathhouse."

Later her colleague Edmund Landau was asked whether Noether was indeed a great woman mathematician, to which he replied: "I can testify that she is a great mathematician, but that she is a woman, I cannot swear."

In addition to suffering discrimination, Noether had much else in common with other women mathematicians through the centuries, such as the fact that she too was the daughter of a mathematics professor. Many mathematicians, of both genders, are from mathematical families, giving rise to lighthearted rumors of a mathematical gene, but in the case of women the percentage is particularly high. The probable explanation is that most women with potential were never exposed to the subject or encouraged to pursue it, whereas those born to professors could hardly avoid being immersed in numbers. Furthermore, Noether, like Hypatia, Agnesi, and most other women mathematicians, never married, largely because it was not socially acceptable for women to pursue such careers and there were few men who were prepared to wed brides with such controversial backgrounds. The great Russian mathematician Sonya Kovalevsky is an exception to this rule, inasmuch as she arranged a marriage of convenience to Vladimir Kovalevsky, a man who was agreeable to a platonic relationship. For both parties the marriage allowed them to escape their families and concentrate on their researches, and in Sonya's case traveling alone around Europe was much easier once she was a respectable married woman.

Of all the European countries France displayed the most chauvinistic attitude toward educated women, declaring that mathematics was unsuitable for women and beyond their mental capacity. Although the salons of Paris dominated the mathematical world for most of the eighteenth and nineteenth centuries, only one woman managed to escape the constraints of French society and establish herself as a great number theorist. Sophie Germain revolutionized the study of Fermat's Last Theorem and made a contribution greater than any of the men who had gone before her.

Sophie Germain was born on April 1, 1776, the daughter of a merchant, Ambroise-François Germain. Outside of her work, her life was to be dominated by the turmoils of the French Revolution — the year she discovered her love of numbers the Bastille was stormed, and her study of calculus was shadowed by the Reign of Terror. Although her father was financially successful, Sophie's family were not members of the aristocracy.

Ladies of Germain's social background were not actively encouraged to study mathematics, but they were expected to have sufficient knowledge of the subject in order to be able to discuss the topic should it arise during polite conversation. To this end a series of textbooks were written to help young women come to grips with the latest developments in mathematics and science. Francesco Algarotti was the author of *Sir Isaac Newton's Philosophy Explain'd for the Use of Ladies*. Because Algarotti believed that women were interested only in romance, he attempted to explain Newton's discoveries through the flirtatious dialogue between a Marquise and her interlocutor. For example, the interlocutor outlines the inverse square law of gravitational attraction, whereupon the Marquise gives her own interpretation on this fundamental law of physics: "I cannot help thinking … that this proportion in the squares of the distances of places … is observed even in love. Thus after eight days' absence love becomes sixty-four times less than it was the first day."

Not surprisingly this gallant genre of books was not responsible for inspiring Sophie Germain's interest in mathematics. The event that changed her life occurred one day when she was browsing in her father's library and chanced upon Jean-Étienne Montucla's book *History of Mathematics*. The chapter that caught her imagination was Montucla's essay on the life of Archimedes. His account of Archimedes' discoveries was undoubtedly interesting, but what particularly kindled her fascination was the story surrounding his death. Archimedes had spent his life at Syracuse, studying mathematics in relative tranquillity, but when he was in his late seventies the peace was shattered by the invading Roman army. Legend has it that during the invasion Archimedes was so engrossed in the study of a geometric figure in the sand that he failed to respond to the questioning of a Roman soldier. As a result he was speared to death.

Germain concluded that if somebody could be so consumed by a geometric problem that it could lead to their death, then mathematics must be the most captivating subject in the world. She immediately set about teaching herself the basics of number theory and calculus, and soon she was working late into the night, studying the works of Euler and Newton. This sudden interest in such an unfeminine subject worried her parents. A friend of the family, Count Guglielmo Libri-Carrucci dalla Sommaja, told how Sophie's father confiscated her candles and clothes and removed any heating in order to discourage her from studying. Only a few years later in Britain, the young mathematician Mary Somerville would also have her candles confiscated by her father, who maintained that "we must put a stop to this, or we shall have Mary in a straitjacket one of these days."

In Germain's case she responded by maintaining a secret cache of candles and wrapping herself in bedclothes. Libri-Carrucci wrote that the winter nights were so cold that the ink froze in the inkwell but Sophie continued regardless. She was described by some people as shy and awkward, but she was also immensely determined and eventually her parents relented and gave Sophie their blessing. Germain never married, and throughout her career her father funded her research. For many years Germain continued to study alone, because there were no mathematicians in the family who could introduce her to the latest ideas and her tutors refused to take her seriously.

Then, in 1794, the École Polytechnique opened in Paris. It was founded as an academy of excellence to train mathematicians and scientists for the nation. This would have been an ideal place for Germain to develop her mathematical skills except for the fact that it was an institution reserved only for men. Her natural shyness prevented her from confronting the academy's governing body, so instead she resorted to covertly studying at the École by assuming the identity of a former student at the academy, Monsieur Antoine-August Le Blanc. The academy's administration was unaware that the real Monsieur Le Blanc had left Paris and continued to print lecture notes and problems for him. Germain managed to obtain what was intended for Le Blanc, and each week she would submit answers to the problems under her new pseudonym.

Everything was going well until a couple of months later when the supervisor of the course, Joseph-Louis Lagrange, could no longer ignore the brilliance of Monsieur Le Blanc's answer sheets. Not only were Monsieur Le Blanc's solutions marvelously ingenious, but they showed a remarkable transformation in a student who had previously been notorious for his abysmal calculations. Lagrange, who was one of the finest mathematicians of the nineteenth century, requested a meeting with the reformed student and Germain was forced to reveal her true identity. Lagrange was astonished and pleased to meet the young woman and became her mentor and friend. At last Sophie Germain had a teacher who could inspire her, and with whom she could be open about her skills and ambitions.

Germain grew in confidence, and she moved from solving problems in her coursework to studying unexplored areas of mathematics. Most important, she became interested in number theory and inevitably she came to hear of Fermat's Last Theorem. She worked on the problem for several years, eventually reaching the stage where she believed she had made an important breakthrough. She needed to discuss her ideas with a fellow number theorist and decided that she would go straight to the top and consult the greatest number theorist in the world, the German mathematician Carl Friedrich Gauss.

Gauss is acknowledged as being one of the most brilliant mathematicians who has ever lived. (While E. T. Bell referred to Fermat as the "Prince of Amateurs," he called Gauss the "Prince of Mathematicians.") Germain had first encountered his work through studying his masterpiece *Disquisitiones arithmeticae*, the most important and wide-ranging treatise since Euclid's *Elements*. Gauss's work influenced every area of mathematics, but strangely enough he never published anything on Fermat's Last Theorem. In one letter he even displayed contempt for the problem. His friend the German astronomer Heinrich Olbers had written to Gauss encouraging him to compete for a prize that had been offered by the Paris Academy for a solution to Fermat's challenge: "It seems to me, dear Gauss, that you should get busy about this." Two weeks later Gauss replied, "I am very much obliged for your news concerning the Paris prize. But I confess that Fermat's Last Theorem as an isolated proposition has very little interest for me, for I could easily lay down a multitude of such propositions, which one could neither prove nor disprove."

Historians suspect that Gauss had tried and failed to make any impact on the problem and his response to Olbers was merely a case of intellectual sour grapes. Nonetheless, when he received Germain's letters he was sufficiently impressed to temporarily forget his ambivalence toward the Last Theorem.

Seventy-five years earlier Euler had published his proof for the case $n = 3$, and ever since mathematicians had been trying in vain to prove other individual cases. However, Germain adopted a new strategy and described to Gauss a so-called general approach to the problem. In other words, her immediate goal was not to prove one particular case, but to say something about many cases at once. In her letter to Gauss she outlined a calculation that focused on a particular type of prime number p such that $(2p + 1)$ is also prime. Germain's list of primes includes 5, because 11 $(2 \times 5 + 1)$ is also prime; but it does not include 13, because 27 $(2 \times 13 + 1)$ is not prime.

For values of n equal to these Germain primes, she used an elegant argument to show that there were probably no solutions to the equation $x^n + y^n = z^n$. By "probably" Germain meant that it was unlikely that any solutions existed, because if there was a solution then either x, y, or z would be a multiple of n, and this would put a very tight restriction on any solutions. Her colleagues examined her list of primes one by one trying to prove that x, y, or z could not be a multiple of n, thereby showing that for that particular value of n there could be no solutions.

In 1825 her method claimed its first complete success thanks to Gustav Lejeune-Dirichlet and Adrien-Marie Legendre, two mathematicians a generation apart. Legendre was a man in his seventies who had lived through the political turmoil of the French Revolution. His failure to support the government candidate for the Institut National led to the stopping of his pension, and by the time he made his contribution to Fermat's Last Theorem he was destitute. On the other hand, Dirichlet was an ambitious young number theorist who had only just turned twenty. Both of them independently were able to prove that the case $n = 5$ has no solutions, but they based their proofs on, and owed their success to, Sophie Germain.

Fourteen years later the French made another breakthrough. Gabriel Lamé made some further ingenious additions to Germain's method and proved the case for the prime $n = 7$. Germain had shown numbers theorists how to destroy an entire section of prime cases, and now it was up to the combined efforts of her colleagues to continue proving Fermat's Last Theorem one case at a time.

Germain's work on the theorem was to be her greatest contribution to mathematics, but initially she was not credited for her breakthrough. When Germain wrote to Gauss she was still in her twenties, and although she had gained a reputation in Paris she feared that the great man would not take her seriously because of her gender. In order to protect herself Germain resorted once again to her pseudonym, signing her letters as Monsieur Le Blanc.

Her fear and respect for Gauss is shown in one of her letters to him: "Unfortunately, the depth of my intellect does not equal the voracity of my appetite, and I feel a kind of temerity in troubling a man of genius when I have no other claim to his attention than an admiration necessarily shared by all his readers." Gauss, unaware of his correspondent's true identity, attempted to put Germain at ease and replied: "I am delighted that arithmetic has found in you so able a friend."

Germain's contribution may have been forever wrongly attributed to the mysterious Monsieur Le Blanc were it not for the Emperor Napoleon. In 1806 Napoleon was invading Prussia and the French army was storming through one German city after another. Germain feared that the fate that befell Archimedes might also take the life of her other great hero, Gauss, so she sent a message to her friend General Joseph-Marie Pernety, who was in charge of the advancing forces. She asked him to guarantee Gauss's safety, and as a result the general took special care of the German mathematician, explaining to him that he owed his life to Mademoiselle Sophie Germain. Gauss was grateful but surprised, for he had never heard of the mysterious lady.

The game was up. In Germain's next letter to Gauss she reluctantly revealed her true identity. Far from being angry at the deception, Gauss wrote back to her with delight:

> But how to describe to you my admiration and astonishment at
> seeing my esteemed correspondent Monsieur Le Blanc
> metamorphose himself into this illustrious personage who gives
> such a brilliant example of what I would find it difficult to
> believe. A taste for the abstract sciences in general and above all
> the mysteries of numbers is excessively rare: one is not astonished
> at it: the enchanting charms of this sublime science reveal
> themselves only to those who have the courage to go deeply into
> it. But when a person of the sex which, according to our customs
> and prejudices, must encounter infinitely more difficulties than
> men to familiarize herself with these thorny researches, succeeds
> nevertheless in surmounting these obstacles and penetrating the
> most obscure parts of them, then without doubt she must have
> the noblest courage, quite extraordinary talents and superior
> genius. Indeed nothing could prove to me in so flattering and
> less equivocal manner that the attractions of this science, which
> has enriched my life with so many joys, are not chimerical, as the
> predilection with which you have honored it.

Sophie Germain's correspondence with Carl Gauss inspired
much of her work, but in 1808 the relationship ended abruptly.
Gauss had been appointed professor of astronomy at the University of Göttingen, his interest shifted from number theory to more
applied mathematics, and he no longer bothered to return
Germain's letters. Without her mentor her confidence began to
wane, and within a year she abandoned pure mathematics.

She embarked on an eventful career as a physicist, a discipline in which she would again excel only to be confronted by
the prejudices of the establishment. Her most important contribution to the subject was "Memoir on the vibrations of elastic

plates," a brilliantly insightful paper that laid the foundations for the modern theory of elasticity. As a result of this research and her work on Fermat's Last Theorem she received a medal from the Institut de France, and became the first woman who was not a wife of a member to attend lectures at the Academy of Sciences. Eventually, toward the end of her life, she reestablished her relationship with Carl Gauss, who convinced the University of Göttingen to award her an honorary degree. Tragically, before the university could bestow the honor upon her, Sophie Germain died of breast cancer.

All things considered she was probably the most profoundly intellectual woman that France has ever produced. And yet, strange as it may seem, when the state official came to make out the death certificate of this eminent associate and co-worker of the most illustrious members of the French Academy of Science, he designated her as a *rentière annuitant* (a single woman with no profession) — not as a *mathématicienne*. Nor is this all. When the Eiffel Tower was erected, in which the engineers were obliged to give special attention to the elasticity of the materials used, there were inscribed on this lofty structure the names of seventy-two savants. But one will not find in this list the name of that daughter of genius, whose researches contributed so much towards establishing the theory of the elasticity of metals — Sophie Germain. Was she excluded from this list for the same reason that Agnesi was ineligible for membership in the French Academy — because she was a woman? It would seem so. If such, indeed, was the case, more is the shame for those who were responsible for such ingratitude towards one who had deserved so well of science, and who by her achievements had won an enviable place in the hall of fame.

H. J. Mozans, 1913

Gabriel Lamé

The Sealed Envelopes

After the breakthrough of Sophie Germain the French Academy of Sciences offered a series of prizes, including a gold medal and 3,000 Francs to the mathematician who could finally put to rest the mystery of Fermat's Last Theorem. As well as the prestige of proving the Last Theorem there was now an immensely valuable reward attached to the challenge. The salons of Paris were full of rumors as to who was adopting which strategy and how close they were to announcing a result. Then, on March 1, 1847, the Academy held its most dramatic meeting ever.

The proceedings describe how Gabriel Lamé, who had proved the case $n = 7$ some years earlier, took the podium in front of the most eminent mathematicians of the age and proclaimed that he was on the verge of proving Fermat's Last Theorem. He admitted that his proof was still incomplete, but he outlined his method and predicted with relish that he would in the coming weeks publish a complete proof in the Academy's journal.

The entire audience was stunned, but as soon as Lamé left the floor Augustin Louis Cauchy, another of Paris's finest mathematicians, asked for permission to speak. Cauchy announced to the Academy that he had been working along similar lines to Lamé, and that he too was about to publish a complete proof.

Both Cauchy and Lamé realized that time was of the essence. Whoever would be first to submit a complete proof would receive the most prestigious and valuable prize in mathematics. Although neither of them had a complete proof, the two rivals were keen to somehow stake a claim and so just three weeks after they had made their announcements they deposited sealed envelopes at the Academy. This was a common practice at the time that enabled mathematicians to go on record without re-

Augustin Cauchy

vealing the exact details of their work. If a dispute should later arise regarding the originality of ideas, then a sealed envelope would provide the evidence needed to establish priority.

The anticipation built up throughout April as Cauchy and Lamé published tantalizing but vague details of their proof in the proceedings of the Academy. Although the entire mathematical community was desperate to see the proof completed, many of them secretly hoped that it would be Lamé and not Cauchy who would win the race. By all accounts Cauchy was a self-righteous creature, a religious bigot and extremely unpopular with his colleagues. He was tolerated at the Academy only because of his brilliance.

Then, on May 24, an announcement was made that put an end to the speculation. It was neither Cauchy nor Lamé who addressed the Academy but rather Joseph Liouville. Liouville shocked the entire audience by reading out the contents of a letter from the German mathematician Ernst Kummer.

Kummer was a number theorist of the highest order, but for much of his career a fierce patriotism fired by a hatred of Napoleon deflected him from his true calling. When Kummer was an infant the French army invaded his hometown of Sorau, bringing with them an epidemic of typhus. Kummer's father was the town physician, and within weeks he was taken by the disease. Traumatized by the experience, Kummer swore to do his utmost to defend his country from further attack, and as soon as he left university he applied his intellect to the problem of plotting the trajectories of cannonballs. Ultimately he taught the laws of ballistics at Berlin's war college.

In parallel with his military career Kummer actively pursued pure mathematical research and had been fully aware of the ongoing saga at the French Academy. He had read through the proceedings and analyzed the few details that Cauchy and Lamé had dared to reveal. To Kummer it was obvious that the two Frenchmen were heading toward the same logical dead end, and he outlined his reasons in the letter that he sent to Liouville.

According to Kummer the fundamental problem was that the proofs of both Cauchy and Lamé relied on using a property of numbers known as unique factorization. Unique factorization states that there is only one possible combination of primes that will multiply together to give any particular number. For instance, the only combination of primes that will build the number 18 is as follows:

$$18 = 2 \times 3 \times 3.$$

Similarly, the following numbers are uniquely factorized in the following ways:

$$35 = 5 \times 7,$$
$$180 = 2 \times 2 \times 3 \times 3 \times 5,$$
$$106{,}260 = 2 \times 2 \times 3 \times 5 \times 7 \times 11 \times 23.$$

Unique factorization was discovered back in the fourth century B.C. by Euclid, who proved that it is true for all counting numbers and described the proof in Book IX of his *Elements*. The fact that unique factorization is true for all counting numbers is a vital element in many other proofs and is nowadays called the *fundamental theorem of arithmetic*.

At first sight there should have been no reason why Cauchy and Lamé should not rely on unique factorization, as had hundreds of mathematicians before them. Unfortunately both of their proofs involved imaginary numbers. Although unique factorization is true for real numbers, Kummer pointed out that it

Ernst Kummer

might not necessarily hold true when imaginary numbers are introduced. According to him this was a fatal flaw.

For example, if we restrict ourselves to real numbers then the number 12 can be factorized only into $2 \times 2 \times 3$. However, if we allow imaginary numbers into our proof then 12 can also be factorized in the following way:

$$12 = (1 + \sqrt{-11}) \times (1 - \sqrt{-11}).$$

Here $(1 + \sqrt{-11})$ is a complex number, a combination of a real and an imaginary number. Although the process of multiplication is more convoluted than for ordinary numbers, the existence of complex numbers does lead to additional ways to factorize 12. Another way to factorize 12 is $(2 + \sqrt{-8}) \times (2 - \sqrt{-8})$. There is no longer a unique factorization but rather a choice of factorizations.

This loss of unique factorization severely damaged the proofs of Cauchy and Lamé, but it did not necessarily destroy them completely. The proofs were supposed to show that there were no solutions to the equation $x^n + y^n = z^n$, where n represents any number greater than 2. As discussed earlier in this chapter, the proof had to work only for the prime values of n. Kummer showed that by employing extra techniques it was possible to restore unique factorization for various values of n. For example, the problem of unique factorization could be circumvented for all prime numbers up to and including $n = 31$. However, the prime number $n = 37$ could not be dealt with so easily. Among the other primes less than 100, two others, $n = 59$ and 67, were also awkward cases. These so-called irregular primes, which are sprinkled throughout the remaining prime numbers, were now the stumbling block to a complete proof.

Kummer pointed out that there was no known mathematics that could tackle all these irregular primes in one fell swoop. However, he did believe that, by carefully tailoring techniques to each individual irregular prime, they could be dealt with one by one. Developing these customized techniques would be a slow and painful exercise, and worse still the number of irregular primes is still infinite. Disposing of them individually would occupy the world's community of mathematicians until the end of time.

Kummer's letter had a devastating effect on Lamé. With hindsight the assumption of unique factorization was at best overoptimistic and at worst foolhardy. Lamé realized that had he been more open about his work he might have spotted the error sooner, and he wrote to his colleague Dirichlet in Berlin: "If only you had been in Paris, or I had been in Berlin, all of this would not have happened."

While Lamé felt humiliated, Cauchy refused to accept defeat. He felt that compared to Lamé's proof his own approach was less reliant on unique factorization, and until Kummer's analysis had been fully checked there was the possibility that it was flawed. For several weeks he continued to publish articles on the subject, but by the end of the summer he too fell silent.

Kummer had demonstrated that a complete proof of Fermat's Last Theorem was beyond the current mathematical approaches. It was a brilliant piece of mathematical logic, but a massive blow to an entire generation of mathematicians who had hoped that they might solve the world's hardest mathematical problem.

The situation was summarized by Cauchy, who in 1857 wrote the Academy's closing report on their prize for Fermat's Last Theorem:

> Report on the competition for the Grand Prize in mathematical sciences. Already set in the competition for 1853 and prorogued to 1856.
>
> Eleven memoirs have been presented to the secretary. But none

has solved the proposed question. Thus, after many times being put forward for a prize, the question remains at the point where Monsieur Kummer left it. However, the mathematical sciences should congratulate themselves for the works which were undertaken by the geometers, with their desire to solve the question, specially by Monsieur Kummer; and the Commissaries think that the Academy would make an honorable and useful decision if, by withdrawing the question from the competition, it would adjugate the medal to Monsieur Kummer, for his beautiful researches on the complex numbers composed of roots of unity and integers.

For over two centuries every attempt to rediscover the proof of Fermat's Last Theorem had ended in failure. Throughout his teenage years Andrew Wiles had studied the work of Euler, Germain, Cauchy, Lamé, and finally Kummer. He hoped he could learn by their mistakes, but by the time he was an undergraduate at the University of Oxford he confronted the same brick wall that faced Kummer.

Some of Wiles's contemporaries were beginning to suspect that the problem might be impossible. Perhaps Fermat had deceived himself and therefore the reason why nobody had rediscovered Fermat's proof was that no such proof existed. Despite this skepticism Wiles continued to search for a proof. He was inspired by the knowledge that there had been several cases in the past of proofs that had eventually been discovered only after centuries of effort. And in some of those cases the flash of insight that solved the problem did not rely on new mathematics; rather, it was a proof that could have been done long ago.

There was a possibility that all the techniques required to prove Fermat's Last Theorem were available, and that the only missing ingredient was ingenuity. Wiles was not prepared to give up: Finding a proof of the Last Theorem had turned from being a childhood fascination into a full-fledged obsession. Having learned all there was to learn about the mathematics of the nineteenth century, Wiles decided to arm himself with techniques of the twentieth century.

Paul Wolfskehl

4

Into Abstraction
· · · · · · · · · · · · · · · ·

> Proof is an idol before which the mathematician tortures
> himself.
>
> Sir Arthur Eddington

Following the work of Ernst Kummer, hopes of finding a proof
for the Last Theorem seemed fainter than ever. Furthermore
mathematics was beginning to move into different areas of study
and there was a risk that the new generation of mathematicians
would ignore what seemed an impossible dead-end problem. By
the end of the nineteenth century the problem still held a special
place in the hearts of number theorists, but they treated Fermat's
Last Theorem in the same way that chemists treated alchemy.
Both were foolish romantic dreams from a past age.

At the turn of the century Paul Wolfskehl, a German industrialist from Darmstadt, gave the problem a new lease on life. The
Wolfskehl family were famous for their wealth and their patron-
age of the arts and sciences, and Paul was no exception. He had
studied mathematics at university and, although he devoted most
of his life to building the family's business empire, he maintained
contact with professional mathematicians and continued to
dabble in number theory. In particular Wolfskehl refused to give
up on Fermat's Last Theorem.

Wolfskehl was by no means a gifted mathematician and he was

not destined to make a major contribution to finding a proof of the Last Theorem. Nonetheless, thanks to a curious chain of events, he was to become forever associated with Fermat's problem, and would inspire thousands of others to take up the challenge.

The story begins with Wolfskehl's obsession with a beautiful woman, whose identity has never been established. Depressingly for Wolfskehl the mysterious woman rejected him and he was left in such a state of utter despair that he decided to commit suicide. He was a passionate man, but not impetuous, and he planned his death with meticulous detail. He set a date for his suicide and would shoot himself through the head at the stroke of midnight. In the days that remained he settled all his outstanding business affairs, and on the final day he wrote his will and composed letters to all his close friends and family.

Wolfskehl had been so efficient that everything was completed slightly ahead of his midnight deadline, so to while away the hours he went to the library and began browsing through the mathematical publications. It was not long before he found himself staring at Kummer's classic paper explaining the failure of Cauchy and Lamé. It was one of the great calculations of the age and suitable reading for the final moments of a suicidal mathematician. Wolfskehl worked through the calculation line by line. Suddenly he was startled at what appeared to be a gap in the logic — Kummer had made an assumption and failed to justify a step in his argument. Wolfskehl wondered whether he had uncovered a serious flaw or whether Kummer's assumption was justified. If the former were true, then there was a chance that proving Fermat's Last Theorem might be a good deal easier than many had presumed.

He sat down, explored the inadequate segment of the proof, and became engrossed in developing a mini-proof that would either consolidate Kummer's work or prove that his assumption was wrong, in which case all Kummer's work would be invalidated. By dawn his work was complete. The bad news, as far as mathematics was concerned, was that Kummer's proof had been remedied and the Last Theorem remained in the realm of the unattainable. The good news was that the appointed time of the suicide had passed, and Wolfskehl was so proud that he had discovered and corrected a gap in the work of the great Ernst Kummer that his despair and sorrow evaporated. Mathematics had renewed his desire for life.

Wolfskehl tore up his farewell letters and rewrote his will in the light of what had happened that night. Upon his death in 1908 the new will was read out, and the Wolfskehl family were shocked to discover that Paul had bequeathed a large proportion of his fortune as a prize to be awarded to whomsoever could prove Fermat's Last Theorem. The reward of 100,000 Marks, approximately the equivalent of a million dollars by today's standards, was his way of repaying a debt to the conundrum that had saved his life.

The money was put into the charge of the *Königliche Gesellschaft der Wissenschaften* of Göttingen, which officially announced the competition for the Wolfskehl Prize that same year:

By the power conferred on us, by Dr. Paul Wolfskehl, deceased in Darmstadt, we hereby fund a prize of one hundred thousand Marks, to be given to the person who will be the first to prove the great theorem of Fermat.

The following rules will be followed:
(1) The *Königliche Gesellschaft der Wissenschaften* in Göttingen will have absolute freedom to decide upon whom the prize should be conferred. It will refuse to accept any manuscript written with the sole aim of entering the competition to obtain the Prize. It will only take into consideration those mathematical memoirs which

have appeared in the form of a monograph in the periodicals, or which are for sale in the bookshops. The Society asks the authors of such memoirs to send at least five printed exemplars.

(2) Works which are published in a language which is not understood by the scholarly specialists chosen for the jury will be excluded from the competition. The authors of such works will be allowed to replace them by translations, of guaranteed faithfulness.

(3) The Society declines responsibility for the examination of works not brought to its attention, as well as for the errors which might result from the fact that the author of a work, or part of a work, are unknown to the Society.

(4) The Society retains the right of decision in the case where various persons would have dealt with the solution of the problem, or for the case where the solution is the result of the combined efforts of several scholars, in particular concerning the partition of the Prize.

(5) The award of the Prize by the Society will take place not earlier than two years after the publication of the memoir to be crowned. The interval of time is intended to allow German and foreign mathematicians to voice their opinion about the validity of the solution published.

(6) As soon as the Prize is conferred by the Society, the laureate will be informed by the secretary, in the name of the Society; the result will be published wherever the Prize has been announced during the preceding year. The assignment of the Prize by the Society is not to be the subject of any further discussion.

(7) The payment of the Prize will be made to the laureate, in the

next three months after the award, by the Royal Cashier of Göttingen University, or, at the receiver's own risk, at any other place he may have designated.

(8) The capital may be delivered against receipt, at the Society's will, either in cash, or by the transfer of financial values. The payment of the Prize will be considered as accomplished by the transmission of these financial values, even though their total value at the day's end may not attain 100,000 Marks.

(9) If the Prize is not awarded by 13 September 2007, no ulterior claim will be accepted.
The competition for the Wolfskehl Prize is open, as of today, under the above conditions.

Göttingen, 27 June 1908
Die Königliche Gesellschaft der Wissenschaften

It is worth noting that although the Committee would give 100,000 Marks to the first mathematician to prove that Fermat's Last Theorem is true, they would not award a single pfennig to anybody who might prove that it is false.

The Wolfskehl Prize was announced in all the mathematical journals and news of the competition rapidly spread across Europe. Despite the publicity campaign and the added incentive of an enormous prize the Wolfskehl Committee failed to arouse a great deal of interest among serious mathematicians. The majority of professional mathematicians viewed Fermat's Last Theorem as a lost cause and decided that they could not afford to waste their careers working on a fool's errand. However, the prize did succeed in introducing the problem to a whole new audience, a horde of eager minds who were willing to apply themselves to the ultimate riddle and approach it from a path of complete innocence.

The Era of Puzzles, Riddles, and Enigmas

Ever since the Greeks, mathematicians have sought to spice up their textbooks by rephrasing proofs and theorems in the form of solutions to number puzzles. During the latter half of the nineteenth century this playful approach to the subject found its way into the popular press, and number puzzles were to be found alongside crosswords and anagrams. In due course there was a growing audience for mathematical conundrums, as amateurs contemplated everything from the most trivial riddles to profound mathematical problems, including Fermat's Last Theorem.

Perhaps the most prolific creator of riddles was Henry Dudeney, who wrote for dozens of newspapers and magazines, including the *Strand, Cassell's*, the *Queen, Tit-Bits*, the *Weekly Dispatch*, and *Blighty*. Another of the great puzzlers of the Victorian Age was the Reverend Charles Dodgson, lecturer in mathematics at Christ Church, Oxford, and better known as the author Lewis Carroll. Dodgson devoted several years to compiling a giant compendium of puzzles entitled *Curiosa Mathematica*, and although the series was not completed he did write several volumes, including *Pillow Problems*.

The greatest riddler of them all was the American prodigy Sam Loyd (1841–1911), who as a teenager was making a healthy profit by creating new puzzles and reinventing old ones. He recalls in *Sam Loyd and his Puzzles: An Autobiographical Review* that some of his early puzzles were created for the circus owner and trickster P. T. Barnum:

> Many years ago, when Barnum's Circus was of a truth "the greatest show on earth," the famous showman got me to prepare for him a series of prize puzzles for advertising purposes. They became

Figure 11. A cartoon reflecting the mania caused by Sam Loyd's "14–15" puzzle.

widely known as the "Questions of the Sphinx," on account of the large prizes offered to anyone who could master them.

Strangely this autobiography was written in 1928, seventeen years after Loyd's death. Loyd passed his cunning on to his son, also called Sam, who was the real author of the book, knowing full well that anybody buying it would mistakenly assume that it had been written by the more famous Sam Loyd Senior.

Loyd's most famous creation was the Victorian equivalent of the Rubik's Cube, the "14–15" puzzle, which is still found in toy shops today. Fifteen tiles numbered 1 to 15 are arranged in a 4×4 grid, and the aim is to slide the tiles and rearrange them into the correct order. Loyd's "14–15" puzzle was sold in the arrangement shown in Figure 11, and he offered a significant reward to whoever could complete the puzzle by swapping the "14" and "15" into their proper positions via any series of tile slides. Loyd's son wrote about the fuss generated by this tangible but essentially mathematical puzzle:

> A prize of $1,000, offered for the first correct solution to the problem, has never been claimed, although there are thousands of persons who say they performed the required feat. People became infatuated with the puzzle and ludicrous tales are told of shopkeepers who neglected to open their stores; of a distinguished clergyman who stood under a street lamp all through a wintry night trying to recall the way he had performed the feat. The mysterious feature of the puzzle is that none seem to be able to remember the sequence of moves whereby they feel sure they succeeded in solving the puzzle. Pilots are said to have wrecked their ships, and engineers rushed their trains past stations. A famous Baltimore editor tells how he went for his noon lunch and was discovered by his frantic staff long past midnight pushing little pieces of pie around on a plate!

Loyd was always confident that he would never have to pay out the $1,000, because he knew that it is impossible to swap just two pieces without destroying the order elsewhere in the puzzle. In the same way that a mathematician can prove that a particular equation has no solutions, Loyd could prove that his "14–15" puzzle is insoluble.

Loyd's proof began by defining a quantity that measured how disordered a puzzle is, the disorder parameter D_p. The disorder parameter for any given arrangement is the number of tile pairs that are in the wrong order, so for the correct puzzle, as shown in Figure 12(a), $D_p = 0$, because no tiles are in the wrong order.

By starting with the ordered puzzle and then sliding the tiles

(a) $D_p = 0$ **(b)** $D_p = 6$ **(c)** $D_p = 12$

Figure 12. By sliding the tiles it is possible to create various disordered arrangements. For each arrangement it is possible to measure the amount of disorder, via the disorder parameter, D_p.

around, it is relatively easy to get to the arrangement shown in Figure 12(b). The tiles are in the correct order until we reach tiles 12 and 11. Obviously the 11 tile should come before the 12 tile, and so this pair of tiles is in the wrong order. The complete list of tile pairs that are in the wrong order is as follows: (12,11), (15,13), (15,14), (15,11), (13,11) and (14,11). With six tile pairs in the wrong order in this arrangement, $D_p = 6$. (Note that tile 10 and tile 12 are next to each other, which is clearly incorrect, but they are not in the wrong order. Therefore this tile pair does not contribute to the disorder parameter.)

After a bit more sliding we get to the arrangement in Figure 12(c). If you compile a list of tile pairs in the wrong order then you will discover that $D_p = 12$. The important point to notice is that in all these cases, (a), (b), and (c), the value of the disorder parameter is an even number (0, 6, and 12). In fact, if you begin with the correct arrangement and proceed to rearrange it, then this statement is always true. As long as the empty square ends up in the bottom right-hand corner, any amount of tile sliding will always result in an even value for D_p. The even value for the disorder parameter is an integral property of any arrangement derived from the original correct arrangement. In mathematics a property that always holds true no matter what is done to the object is called an *invariant*.

However, if you examine the arrangement that was being sold by Loyd, in which the 14 and 15 were swapped, then the value of the disorder parameter is one, D_p =1, i.e., the only pair of tiles out of order are the 14 and 15. For Loyd's arrangement the disorder parameter has an odd value! Yet we know that any arrangement derived from the correct arrangement has an even value for the disorder parameter. The conclusion is that Loyd's arrangement cannot be derived from the correct arrangement, and conversely it is impossible to get from Loyd's arrangement back to the correct one — Loyd's $1,000 was safe.

Loyd's puzzle and the disorder parameter demonstrate the power of an invariant. Invariants provide mathematicians with an important strategy to prove that it is impossible to transform one object into another. For example, an area of current excitement concerns the study of knots, and naturally knot theorists are interested in trying to prove whether or not one knot can be transformed into another by twisting and looping but without cutting. In order to answer this question they attempt to find a property of the first knot that cannot be destroyed no matter how much twisting and looping occurs — a knot invariant. They then calculate the same property for the second knot. If the values are different then the conclusion is that it must be impossible to get from the first knot to the second.

Until this technique was invented in the 1920s by Kurt Reidemeister it was impossible to prove that one knot could not be transformed into any other knot. In other words before knot invariants were discovered it was impossible to prove that a granny knot is fundamentally different from a reef knot, an overhand knot, or even a simple loop with no knot at all. The concept of an invariant property is central to many other mathematical proofs and, as we shall see in Chapter 5, it would be crucial in bringing Fermat's Last Theorem back into the mainstream of mathematics.

By the turn of the century, thanks to the likes of Sam Loyd and his "14–15" puzzle, there were millions of amateur problem-solvers throughout Europe and America eagerly looking for new challenges. Once news of Wolfskehl's legacy filtered down to these budding mathematicians, Fermat's Last Theorem was again the world's most famous problem. The Last Theorem was infinitely more complex than even the hardest of Loyd's puzzles, but the prize was vastly greater. Amateurs dreamed that they might be able to find a relatively simple trick that had eluded the great professors of the past. The keen twentieth-century amateur was to a large extent on a par with Pierre de Fermat when it came to knowledge of mathematical techniques. The challenge was to match the creativity with which Fermat used his techniques.

Although all entries for the Wolfskehl Prize were supposed to have been published in math journals, this did not prevent amateurs from sending an avalanche of entries into the University of Göttingen. Not surprisingly all the proofs were fallacious. Although each entrant was convinced that they had solved this centuries-old problem they had all made subtle, and sometimes not so subtle, errors in their logic. The art of number theory is so abstract that it is frighteningly easy to wander off the path of logic and be completely unaware that one has strayed into absurdity. Appendix 6 shows the sort of classic error that can easily be overlooked by an enthusiastic amateur.

Regardless of who had sent in a particular proof, every single one of them had to be scrupulously checked just in case an unknown amateur had stumbled upon the most sought after proof in mathematics. The head of the mathematics department at Göttingen between 1909 and 1934 was Professor Edmund Landau, and it was his responsibility to examine the entries for the Wolfskehl Prize. Landau found that his research was being continually interrupted by having to deal with the dozens of confused proofs that arrived on his desk each month. To cope with the situation he invented a neat method of off-loading the work. The professor printed hundreds of cards that read:

Dear ....,

Thank you for your manuscript on the proof of Fermat's Last Theorem.
The first mistake is on :
Page .... Line ....
This invalidates the proof.

Professor E. M. Landau

Landau would then hand each new entry, along with a printed card, to one of his students and ask them to fill in the blanks.

The entries continued unabated for years, even following the dramatic devaluation of the Wolfskehl Prize — the result of the hyperinflation that followed the First World War. There are rumors that say that anyone winning the competition today would hardly be able to purchase a cup of coffee with the prize money, but these claims are somewhat exaggerated.

Dr. F. Schlichting, who was responsible for dealing with entries during the 1970s, wrote a letter to Paulo Ribenboim explaining that the prize was then still worth over 10,000 Marks. See Appendix 7 for the text of Schlichting's letter. It gives a unique insight into the work of the Wolfskehl committee.

Competitors did not restrict themselves to sending "solutions" to Göttingen, and every mathematics department in the world probably has its cupboard of purported proofs from amateurs. While most institutions ignore these amateur proofs, other recipients have dealt with them in more imaginative ways. The mathematical writer Martin Gardner recalls a friend who would send back a note explaining that he was not competent to examine the proof. Instead he would provide them with the name and address of an expert in the field who could help — that is to say, the details of the last amateur to send him a proof. Another of his friends would write: "I have a remarkable refutation of your attempted proof, but unfortunately this page is not large enough to contain it."

Although amateur mathematicians around the world have spent this century trying and failing to prove Fermat's Last Theorem and win the Wolfskehl Prize, the professionals have continued largely to ignore the problem. Instead of building on the work of Kummer and the other nineteenth-century number theorists, mathematicians began to examine the foundations of their subject in order to address some of the most fundamental questions about numbers. Some of the greatest figures of the twentieth century, including David Hilbert and Kurt Gödel, tried to understand the most profound properties of numbers in order to grasp their true meaning and to discover what questions number theory can and, more important, cannot answer. Their work would shake the foundations of mathematics and ultimately have repercussions for Fermat's Last Theorem.

The Foundations of Knowledge

For hundreds of years mathematicians had been busy using logical proof to build from the known into the unknown. Progress had been phenomenal, with each new generation of mathematicians expanding on their grand structure and creating new concepts of number and geometry. However, toward the end of the nineteenth century, instead of looking forward, mathematical logicians began to look back to the foundations of mathematics upon which everything else was built. They wanted to verify the fundamentals of mathematics and rigorously rebuild everything from first principles, in order to reassure themselves that those first principles were reliable.

Mathematicians are notorious for being sticklers when it comes to requiring absolute proof before accepting any statement. Their reputation is clearly expressed in a story told by Ian Stewart in *Concepts of Modern Mathematics*:

> An astronomer, a physicist, and a mathematician (it is said) were holidaying in Scotland. Glancing from a train window, they observed a black sheep in the middle of a field. "How interesting," observed the astronomer, "all Scottish sheep are black!" To which the physicist responded, "No, no! Some Scottish sheep are black!" The mathematician gazed heavenward in supplication, and then intoned, "In Scotland there exists at least one field, containing at least one sheep, *at least one side of which is black*."

Even more rigorous than the ordinary mathematician is the mathematician who specializes in the study of mathematical logic. Mathematical logicians began to question ideas that other mathematicians had taken for granted for centuries. For example, the law of trichotomy states that every number is either negative, positive, or zero. This seems to be obvious, and mathematicians had tacitly assumed it to be true, but nobody had ever bothered to prove that this really was the case. Logicians realized that, until the law of trichotomy had been proved true, then it might be false, and if that turned out to be the case then an entire edifice of knowledge, everything that relied on the law, would collapse. Fortunately for mathematics, at the end of the last century the law of trichotomy was proved to be true.

Ever since the ancient Greeks, mathematics had been accumulating more and more theorems and truths, and although most of them had been rigorously proved mathematicians were concerned that some of them, such as the law of trichotomy, had crept in without being properly examined. Some ideas had become part of the folklore and yet nobody was quite sure how they had been originally proved, if indeed they ever had been, so logicians decided to prove every theorem from first principles. However, every truth had to be deduced from other truths. Those truths, in turn, first had to be proved from even more fundamental truths, and so on. Eventually the logicians found themselves dealing with a few essential statements that were so fundamental that they themselves could not be proved. These fundamental assumptions are the axioms of mathematics.

One example of the axioms is the *commutative law of addition*, which simply states that, for any numbers m and n,

$$m + n = n + m.$$

This and the handful of other axioms are taken to be self-evident, and can easily be tested by applying them to particular numbers. So far the axioms have passed every test and have been accepted as being the bedrock of mathematics. The challenge for the logicians was to rebuild all of mathematics from these axioms.

Appendix 8 defines the set of arithmetic axioms and gives an idea of how logicians set about building the rest of mathematics.

A legion of logicians participated in the slow and painful process of rebuilding the immensely complex body of mathematical knowledge using only a minimal number of axioms. The idea was to consolidate what mathematicians thought they already knew by employing only the most rigorous standards of logic. The German mathematician Hermann Weyl summarized the mood of the time: "Logic is the hygiene the mathematician practices to keep his ideas healthy and strong." In addition to cleansing what was known, the hope was that this fundamentalist approach would also throw light on as yet unsolved problems, including Fermat's Last Theorem.

The effort to logically rebuild mathematical knowledge was headed by the most eminent figure of the age, David Hilbert. Hilbert believed that everything in mathematics could and should be proved from the basic axioms. The result of this would be to demonstrate conclusively the two most important elements of the mathematical system. First, mathematics should, at least in theory, be able to answer every single question — this is the same ethos of completeness that had in the past demanded the invention of new numbers like the negatives and the imaginaries. Second, mathematics should be free of inconsistencies — that is to say, having shown that a statement is true by one method, it should not be possible to show that the same statement is false via another method. Hilbert was convinced that, by assuming just a few axioms, it would be possible to answer any imaginable mathematical question without fear of contradiction.

On August 8, 1900, Hilbert gave a historic talk at the International Congress of Mathematicians in Paris. Hilbert posed twenty-three unsolved problems in mathematics that he believed were of

David Hilbert

the most immediate importance. Some of the problems related to more general areas of mathematics, but most of them concentrated on the logical foundations of the subject. These problems were intended to focus the attention of the mathematical world and provide a program of research. Hilbert wanted to galvanize the community into helping him realize his vision of a mathematical system free of doubt and inconsistency — an ambition he would have inscribed on his tombstone:

> *Wir müssen wissen,*
> *Wir werden wissen.*

> We must know,
> We will know.

For the next two decades mathematicians tried to establish a flawless mathematical edifice, and by the time Hilbert retired in 1930 he felt confident that mathematics was well on the road to recovery. His dream of a consistent logic, powerful enough to answer every question, was apparently on its way to becoming a reality.

Then in 1931 an unknown twenty-five-year-old mathematician published a paper that would forever destroy Hilbert's hopes. Kurt Gödel would force mathematicians to accept that mathematics could never be logically perfect, and implicit in his works was the idea that problems like Fermat's Last Theorem might even be impossible to solve.

Kurt Gödel was born on April 28, 1906, in Moravia, then part of the Austro-Hungarian Empire, now part of the Czech Republic. As a child Gödel displayed a talent for science and mathematics, and his inquisitive nature led his family to nickname him *der Herr Warum* (Mr. Why). He went to the University of Vienna unsure of whether to specialize in mathematics or physics, but an inspiring and passionate lecture course on number theory by Professor P. Furtwängler persuaded Gödel to devote his life to numbers. The lectures were all the more extraordinary because Furtwängler was paralyzed from the neck down and had to lecture from his wheelchair without notes while his assistant wrote on the blackboard.

By his early twenties Gödel had established himself in the mathematics department, but along with his colleagues he would occasionally wander down the corridor to attend meetings of the *Wiener Kreis* (Viennese Circle), a group of philosophers who would gather to discuss the day's great questions of logic. It was during this period that Gödel developed the ideas that would devastate the foundations of mathematics.

In 1931 Gödel published his book *Über formal unentscheidbare Sätze der Principia Mathematica und verwandter Systeme* (On Formally Undecidable Propositions in *Principia Mathematica* and Related Systems), which contained his so-called theorems of undecidability. When news of the theorems reached America the great mathematician John von Neumann immediately canceled a lecture series he was giving on Hilbert's program and replaced the remainder of the course with a discussion of Gödel's revolutionary work.

Gödel had proved that trying to create a complete and consistent mathematical system was an impossible task. His ideas could be encapsulated in two statements.

First theorem of undecidability
If axiomatic set theory is consistent, there exist theorems that can neither be proved or disproved.

Second theorem of undecidability
There is no constructive procedure that will prove axiomatic theory to be consistent.

Kurt Gödel

Essentially Gödel's first statement said that no matter what set of axioms were being used there would be questions that mathematics could not answer — completeness could never be achieved. Worse still, the second statement said that mathematicians could never even be sure that their choice of axioms would not lead to a contradiction — consistency could never be proved. Gödel had shown that the Hilbert program was an impossible exercise.

Although Gödel's second statement said that it was impossible to prove that the axioms were consistent, this did not necessarily mean that they were inconsistent. In their hearts many mathematicians still believed that their mathematics would remain consistent, but in their minds they could not prove it. Many years later the great number theorist André Weil would say: "God exists since mathematics is consistent, and the Devil exists since we cannot prove it."

To better understand Gödel's first theorem, its origins and its implications, it is useful to examine a closely related piece of ancient Greek logic known as the *Cretan paradox*, or *liar's paradox*, invented by Epimenides, a Cretan who exclaimed:

"I am a liar!"

The paradox arises when we try to determine whether this statement is true or false. First let us see what happens if we assume that the statement is true. A true statement implies that Epimenides is a liar, but we initially assumed that he made a true statement and therefore Epimenides is not a liar — we have an inconsistency. On the other hand, let us see what happens if we assume that the statement is false. A false statement implies that Epimenides is not a liar, but we initially assumed that he made a false statement and therefore Epimenides is a liar — we have another inconsistency. Whether we assume that the statement is true or false we end up with an inconsistency, and therefore the statement is neither true nor false.

Gödel reinterpreted the liar's paradox and introduced the concept of proof. The result was a statement along the following lines:

This statement does not have any proof.

If the statement were false then the statement would be provable, but this would contradict the statement. Therefore the statement must be true in order to avoid the contradiction. However, although the statement is true it cannot be proven, because this statement (which we now know to be true) says so.

Because Gödel could translate the above statement into mathematical notation, he was able to demonstrate that there existed statements in mathematics that are true but that could never be proven to be true, so-called undecidable statements. This was the deathblow for the Hilbert program.

In many ways Gödel's work paralleled similar discoveries being made in quantum physics. Just four years before Gödel published his work on undecidability, the German physicist Werner Heisenberg uncovered the uncertainty principle. Just as there was a fundamental limit to what theorems mathematicians could prove, Heisenberg showed that there was a fundamental limit to what properties physicists could measure. For example, if they wanted to measure the exact position of an object, then they could measure the object's velocity with only relatively poor accuracy. This is because in order to measure the position of the object it would be necessary to illuminate it with photons of light, but to pinpoint its exact locality the photons of light would have to have enormous energy. However, if the object is being bombarded by high-energy photons its own velocity will be affected and becomes inherently uncertain. Hence, by demanding knowledge of an object's position, physicists would have to give up some knowledge of its velocity.

Heisenberg's uncertainty principle reveals itself only at atomic scales, when high-precision measurements become critical. Therefore much of physics could carry on regardless while quantum physicists concerned themselves with profound questions about the limits of knowledge. The same was happening in the world of mathematics. While the logicians concerned themselves with a highly esoteric debate about undecidability, the rest of the mathematical community carried on regardless. Although Gödel had proved that there were some statements that could not be proven, there were plenty of statements that could be proven and his discovery did not invalidate anything proven in the past. Furthermore, many mathematicians believed that Gödel's undecidable statements would only be found in the most obscure and extreme regions of mathematics and might therefore never be encountered. After all Gödel had said only that these undecidable statements existed; he could not actually point to one. Then in 1963 Gödel's theoretical nightmare became a full-blooded reality.

Paul Cohen, a twenty-nine-year-old mathematician at Stanford University, developed a technique for testing whether or not a particular question is undecidable. The technique works only in a few very special cases, but he was nevertheless the first person to discover specific questions that were indeed undecidable. Having made his discovery, Cohen immediately flew to Princeton, proof in hand, to have it verified by Gödel himself. Two days after receiving his papers, Gödel gave Cohen his stamp of authority. What was particularly dramatic was that some of these undecidable questions were central to mathematics. Ironically Cohen proved that one of the questions that David Hilbert declared to be among the twenty-three most important problems in mathematics, the continuum hypothesis, was undecidable.

Gödel's work, compounded by Cohen's undecidable statements, sent a disturbing message to all those mathematicians, professional and amateur, who were persisting in their attempts to prove Fermat's Last Theorem — perhaps the theorem was undecidable! What if Pierre de Fermat had made a mistake when he claimed to have found a proof? If so, then there was the possibility that the Last Theorem was undecidable. Proving Fermat's Last Theorem might be more than just difficult, it might be impossible. If the theorem were undecidable, then mathematicians had spent centuries in search of a proof that did not exist.

Curiously if Fermat's Last Theorem turned out to be undecidable, then this would imply that it must be true. The reason is as follows. The theorem says that there are no whole number solutions to the equation

$$x^n + y^n = z^n \text{ for } n \text{ greater than 2.}$$

If the Last Theorem were in fact false, then it would be possible to prove this by identifying a solution (a counterexample). Therefore the Last Theorem would be decidable. Being false would be inconsistent with being undecidable. However, if the Last Theorem were true, there would not necessarily be such an unequivocal way of proving it, i.e., it could be undecidable. In conclusion, Fermat's Last Theorem might be true, but there may be no way of proving it.

The Compulsion of Curiosity

Pierre de Fermat's casual jotting in the margin of Diophantus's *Arithmetica* had led to the most infuriating riddle in history. Despite three centuries of glorious failure and Gödel's suggestion that they might be hunting for a nonexistent proof, some mathematicians continued to be attracted to the problem. The Last Theorem was a mathematical siren, luring geniuses toward it, only to dash their hopes. Any mathematician who got involved with Fermat's Last Theorem risked wasting their career, and yet whoever could make the crucial breakthrough would go down in history as having solved the world's most difficult problem.

Generations of mathematicians were obsessed with Fermat's Last Theorem for two reasons. First, there was the ruthless sense of one-upmanship. The Last Theorem was the ultimate test and whoever could prove it would succeed where Cauchy, Euler, Kummer, and countless others had failed. Just as Fermat himself took great pleasure in solving problems that baffled his contemporaries, whoever could prove the Last Theorem could enjoy the fact that they had solved a problem that had confounded the entire community of mathematicians for hundreds of years. Second, whoever could meet Fermat's challenge could enjoy the innocent satisfaction of solving a riddle. The delight derived from solving esoteric questions in number theory is not so different from the simple joy of tackling the trivial riddles of Sam Loyd. A mathematician once said to me that the pleasure he got from solving mathematical problems is similar to that gained by crossword addicts. Filling in the last clue of a particularly tough crossword is always a satisfying experience, but imagine the sense of achievement after spending years on a puzzle, which nobody else in the world has been able to solve, and then figuring out the solution.

These are the same reasons why Andrew Wiles became fascinated by Fermat: "Pure mathematicians just love a challenge. They love unsolved problems. When doing math there's this great feeling. You start with a problem that just mystifies you. You can't understand it, it's so complicated, you just can't make head nor tail of it. But then, when you finally resolve it, you have this incredible feeling of how beautiful it is, how it all fits together so elegantly. Most deceptive are the problems that look easy and yet turn out to be extremely intricate. Fermat is the most beautiful example of this. It just looked as though it had to have a solution and, of course, it's very special because Fermat said that he had a solution."

Mathematics has its applications in science and technology, but that is not what drives mathematicians. They are inspired by the joy of discovery. G. H. Hardy tried to explain and justify his own career in a book entitled *A Mathematician's Apology*:

> I will only say that if a chess problem is, in the crude sense, "useless," then that is equally true of most of the best mathematics . . . I have never done anything "useful." No discovery of mine has made, or is likely to make, directly or indirectly, for good or ill, the least difference to the amenity of the world. Judged by all practical standards, the value of my mathematical life is nil; and outside mathematics it is trivial anyhow. I have just one chance of escaping a verdict of complete triviality, that I may be judged to have created something worth creating. And that I have created something is undeniable: the question is about its value.

The desire for a solution to any mathematical problem is largely fired by curiosity, and the reward is the simple but enormous satisfaction derived from solving any riddle. The mathematician E. C. Titchmarsh once said: "It can be of no practical use to know that π is irrational, but if we can know, it surely would be intolerable not to know."

In the case of Fermat's Last Theorem there was no shortage of curiosity. Gödel's work on undecidability had introduced an element of doubt as to whether the problem was soluble, but this was not enough to discourage the true Fermat fanatic. What was more dispiriting was the fact that by the 1930s mathematicians had exhausted all their techniques and had little else at their disposal. What was needed was a new tool, something that would raise mathematical morale. The Second World War was to provide just what was required — the greatest leap in calculating power since the invention of the slide rule.

The Brute Force Approach

When in 1940 G. H. Hardy declared that the best mathematics is largely useless, he was quick to add that this was not necessarily a bad thing: "Real mathematics has no effects on war. No one has yet discovered any warlike purpose to be served by the theory of numbers." Hardy was soon to be proved wrong.

In 1944 John von Neumann cowrote the book *The Theory of Games and Economic Behavior,* in which he coined the term *game theory.* Game theory was von Neumann's attempt to use mathematics to describe the structure of games and how humans play them. He began by studying chess and poker, and then went on to try to model more sophisticated games such as economics. After the Second World War the RAND corporation realized the potential of von Neumann's ideas and hired him to work on developing Cold War strategies. From that point on, mathematical game theory has become a basic tool for generals to test their military strategies by treating battles as complex games of chess. A simple illustration of the application of game theory in battles is the story of the *truel*.

A truel is similar to a duel, except there are three participants rather than two. One morning Mr. Black, Mr. Gray, and Mr. White decide to resolve a conflict by trueling with pistols until only one of them survives. Mr. Black is the worst shot, hitting his target on average only one time in three. Mr. Gray is a better shot, hitting his target two times out of three. Mr. White is the best shot, hitting his target every time. To make the truel fairer Mr. Black is allowed to shoot first, followed by Mr. Gray (if he is still alive), followed by Mr. White (if he is still alive), and around again until only one of them is alive. The question is this: Where should Mr. Black aim his first shot? You might like to make a guess based on intuition, or better still, based on game theory. The answer is discussed in Appendix 9.

Even more influential in wartime than game theory is the mathematics of code breaking. During the Second World War the Allies realized that in theory mathematical logic could be used to unscramble German messages, if only the calculations could be performed quickly enough. The challenge was to find a way of automating mathematics so that a machine could perform the calculations, and the Englishman who contributed most to this code-cracking effort was Alan Turing.

In 1938 Turing returned to Cambridge having completed a stint at Princeton University. He had witnessed firsthand the turmoil caused by Gödel's theorems of undecidability and had become involved in trying to pick up the pieces of Hilbert's

Alan Turing

dream. In particular he wanted to know if there was a way to define which questions were and were not decidable, and tried to develop a methodical way of answering this question. At the time calculating devices were primitive and effectively useless when it came to serious mathematics, and so instead Turing based his ideas on the concept of an imaginary machine that was capable of infinite computation. This hypothetical machine, which consumed infinite amounts of imaginary ticker tape and could compute for an eternity, was all that he required to explore his abstract questions of logic. What Turing was unaware of was that his imagined mechanization of hypothetical questions would eventually lead to a breakthrough in performing real calculations on real machines.

Despite the outbreak of war, Turing continued his research as a fellow of King's College, until on September 4, 1940, his contented life as a Cambridge don came to an abrupt end. He had been commandeered by the Government Code and Cypher School, whose task it was to unscramble the enemy's coded messages. Prior to the war the Germans had devoted considerable effort to developing a superior system of encryption, and this was a matter of grave concern to British Intelligence, who had in the past been able to decipher their enemy's communications with relative ease. The HMSO's official war history *British Intelligence in the Second World War* describes the state of play in the 1930s:

> By 1937 it was established that, unlike their Japanese and Italian counterparts, the German army, the German navy and probably the air force, together with other state organizations like the railways and the SS used, for all except their tactical communications, different versions of the same cypher system — the Enigma machine which had been put on the market in the

1920s but which the Germans had rendered more secure by progressive modifications. In 1937 the Government Code and Cypher School broke into the less modified and less secure model of this machine that was being used by the Germans, the Italians and the Spanish nationalist forces. But apart from this the Enigma still resisted attack, and it seemed likely that it would continue to do so.

The Enigma machine consisted of a keyboard connected to a scrambler unit. The scrambler unit contained three separate rotors, and the positions of the rotors determined how each letter on the keyboard would be enciphered. What made the Enigma code so difficult to crack was the enormous number of ways in which the machine could be set up. First, the three rotors in the machine were chosen from a selection of five, and could be changed and swapped around to confuse the code-breakers. Second, each rotor could be positioned in one of twenty-six different ways. This means that the machine could be set up in over a million different ways. In addition to the permutations provided by the rotors, plugboard connections at the back of the machine could be changed by hand to provide a total of over 150 million million million possible setups. To increase security even further, the three rotors were continually changing their orientation, so that every time a letter was transmitted, the setup for the machine, and therefore the encipherment, would change for the next letter. So typing "DODO" could generate the message "FGTB" — the "D" and the "O" are sent twice, but encoded differently each time.

Enigma machines were given to the German army, navy, and air force, and were even operated by the railways and other government departments. As with all code systems used during this period, a weakness of the Enigma was that the receiver had to know the sender's Enigma setting. To maintain security the Enigma settings had to be changed on a daily basis. One way for senders to change settings regularly and keep receivers informed was to publish the daily settings in a secret codebook. The risk with this approach was that the British might capture a U-boat and obtain the codebook with all the daily settings for the following month. The alternative approach, and the one adopted for the bulk of the war, was to transmit the daily settings in a preamble to the actual message, encoded using the previous day's settings.

When the war started, the British Cypher School was dominated by classicists and linguists. The Foreign Office soon realized that number theorists had a better chance of finding the key to cracking the German codes and, to begin with, nine of Britain's most brilliant number theorists were gathered at the Cypher School's new home at Bletchley Park, a Victorian mansion in Bletchley, Buckinghamshire. Turing had to abandon his hypothetical machines with infinite ticker tape and endless processing time and come to terms with a practical problem with finite resources and a very real deadline.

Cryptography is an intellectual battle between the codemaker and the code-breaker. The challenge for the codemaker is to shuffle and scramble an outgoing message to the point where it would be indecipherable if intercepted by the enemy. However, there is a limit on the amount of mathematical manipulation possible because of the need to dispatch messages quickly and efficiently. The strength of the German Enigma code was that the coded message underwent several levels of encryption at very high speed. The challenge for the code-breaker was to take an intercepted message and to crack the code while the contents of the message were still relevant. A

German message ordering a British ship to be destroyed had to be decoded before the ship was sunk.

Turing led a team of mathematicians who attempted to build mirror images of the Enigma machine. He incorporated his prewar abstract ideas into these devices, which could in theory methodically check all the possible Enigma machine set-ups until the code was cracked. The British machines, over two meters tall and equally wide, employed electromechanical relays to check all the potential Enigma settings. The constant ticking of the relays led to their being nicknamed *bombes*. Despite their speed it was impossible for the bombes to check every one of the 150 million million million possible Enigma settings within a reasonable amount of time, and so Turing's team had to find ways to significantly reduce the number of permutations by gleaning whatever information they could from the sent messages.

One of the greatest breakthroughs made by the British was the realization that the Enigma machine could never encode a letter into itself, i.e., if the sender tapped "R" then the machine could potentially send out any letter, depending on the settings of the machine, apart from "R." This apparently innocuous fact was all that was needed to drastically reduce the time required to decipher a message. The Germans fought back by limiting the length of the messages they sent. All messages inevitably contain clues for the team of code-breakers, and the longer the message, the more clues it contains. By limiting all messages to a maximum of 250 letters, the Germans hoped to compensate for the Enigma machine's reluctance to encode a letter as itself.

In order to crack codes Turing would often try to guess key words in messages. If he was right it would speed up enormously the cracking of the rest of the code. For example, if the code-breakers suspected that a message contained a weather report, a frequent type of coded report, then they would guess that the message contained words such as "fog" or "windspeed." If they were right they could quickly crack that message, and thereby deduce the Enigma settings for that day. For the rest of the day, other, more valuable, messages could be broken with ease.

When they failed to guess weather words, the British would try to put themselves in the position of the German Enigma operators to guess other key words. A sloppy operator might address the receiver by a first name or he might have developed idiosyncrasies that were known to the codebreakers. When all else failed and German traffic was flowing unchecked, it is said that the British Cypher School even resorted to asking the RAF to mine a particular German harbor. Immediately the German harbormaster would send an encrypted message that would be intercepted by the British. The code-breakers could be confident that the message contained words like "mine," "avoid," and "map reference." Having cracked this message, Turing would have that day's Enigma settings and any further German traffic was vulnerable to rapid decipherment.

On February 1, 1942, the Germans added a fourth wheel to Enigma machines that were employed for sending particularly sensitive information. This was the greatest escalation in the level of encryption during the war, but eventually Turing's team fought back by increasing the efficiency of the bombes. Thanks to the Cypher School, the Allies knew more about their enemy than the Germans could ever have suspected. The impact of German U-boats in the Atlantic was greatly reduced and the British had advanced warning of attacks by the Luftwaffe. The code-breakers also intercepted and deciphered the exact position of German supply ships, allowing British destroyers to find and sink them.

At all times the Allied forces had to take care that their evasive actions and uncanny attacks did not betray their ability to decipher German communications. If the Germans suspected that Enigma had been broken then they would increase their level of encryption, and the British might be back to square one. Hence there were occasions when the Cypher School informed the Allies of an imminent attack, and the Allies chose not to take extreme countermeasures. There are even rumors that Churchill knew that Coventry was to be targeted for a devastating raid, yet he chose not to take special precautions in case the Germans became suspicious. Stuart Milner-Barry, who worked with Turing, denies the rumor, and states that the relevant message concerning Coventry was not cracked until it was too late.

The restrained use of decoded information worked perfectly. Even when the British used intercepted communications to inflict heavy losses, the Germans did not suspect that the Enigma code had been broken. They believed that their level of encryption was so high that it would be absolutely impossible to crack their codes. Instead they blamed any exceptional losses on the British secret service infiltrating their own ranks.

Because of the secrecy surrounding the work carried out at Bletchley by Turing and his team, their immense contribution to the war effort could never be publicly acknowledged, even for many years after the war. It used to be said that the First World War was the chemists' war and that the Second World War was the physicists' war. In fact, from the information revealed in recent decades, it is probably true to say that the Second World War was also the mathematicians' war — and in the case of a third world war their contribution would be even more critical.

Throughout his code-breaking career Turing never lost sight of his mathematical goals. The hypothetical machines had been replaced with real ones, but the esoteric questions remained. By the end of the war Turing had helped build Colossus, a fully electronic machine consisting of 1500 valves, which were much faster than the electromechanical relays employed in the bombes. Colossus was a computer in the modern sense of the word, and with the extra speed and sophistication Turing began to think of it as a primitive brain — it had a memory, it could process information, and states within the computer resembled states of mind. Turing had transformed his imaginary machine into the first real computer.

When the war ended Turing continued to build increasingly complex machines, such as the Automatic Computing Engine (ACE). In 1948 he moved to Manchester University and built the world's first computer to have an electronically stored program. Turing had provided Britain with the most advanced computers in the world, but he would not live long enough to see their most remarkable calculations.

In the years after the war Turing had been under surveillance from British Intelligence, who were aware that he was a practicing homosexual. They were concerned that the man who knew more about Britain's security codes than anyone else was vulnerable to blackmail and decided to monitor his every move. Turing had largely come to terms with being constantly shadowed, but in 1952 he was arrested for violation of British homosexuality statutes. This humiliation made life intolerable for Turing. Andrew Hodges, Turing's biographer, describes the events leading up to his death:

Alan Turing's death came as a shock to those who knew him . . .
That he was an unhappy, tense, person; that he was consulting a
psychiatrist and suffered a blow that would have felled many
people — all this was clear. But the trial was two years in the past,
the hormone treatment had ended a year before, and he seemed
to have risen above it all.

The inquest, on 10 June 1954, established that it was suicide.
He had been found lying neatly in his bed. There was froth
round his mouth, and the pathologist who did the post-mortem
easily identified the cause of death as cyanide poisoning . . . In
the house was a jar of potassium cyanide, and also a jar of
cyanide solution. By the side of his bed was half an apple, out of
which several bites had been taken. They did not analyze the
apple, and so it was never properly established that, as seemed
perfectly obvious, the apple had been dipped in the cyanide.

Turing's legacy was a machine that could take an impractically
long calculation, if performed by a human, and complete it in a
matter of hours. Today's computers perform more calculations
in a split second than Fermat performed in his entire career.
Mathematicians who were still struggling with Fermat's Last
Theorem began to use computers to attack the problem, relying
on a computerized version of Kummer's nineteenth-century approach.

Kummer, having discovered a flaw in the work of Cauchy and
Lamé, showed that the outstanding problem in proving
Fermat's Last Theorem was disposing of the cases when n equals
an irregular prime — for values of n up to 100 the only irregular
primes are 37, 59, and 67. At the same time Kummer showed
that in theory all irregular primes could be dealt with on an
individual basis, the only problem being that each one would
require an enormous amount of calculation. To make his point

Kummer and his colleague Dimitri Mirimanoff put in the weeks of calculation required to dispel the three irregular primes less than 100. However, they and other mathematicians were not prepared to begin on the next batch of irregular primes between 100 and 1,000.

A few decades later the problems of immense calculation began to vanish. With the arrival of the computer awkward cases of Fermat's Last Theorem could be dispatched with speed, and after the Second World War teams of computer scientists and mathematicians proved the Last Theorem for all values of n up to 500, then 1,000, and then 10,000. In the 1980s Samuel S. Wagstaff of the University of Illinois raised the limit to 25,000, and more recently mathematicians could claim that Fermat's Last Theorem was true for all values of n up to 4 million.

Although outsiders felt that modern technology was at last getting the better of the Last Theorem, the mathematical community were aware that their success was purely cosmetic. Even if supercomputers spent decades proving one value of n after another they could never prove every value of n up to infinity, and therefore they could never claim to prove the entire theorem. Even if the theorem was to be proved true for up to a billion, there is no reason why it should be true for a billion and one. If the theorem was to be proved up to a trillion, there is no reason why it should be true for a trillion and one, and so on *ad infinitum.* Infinity is unobtainable by the mere brute force of computerized number crunching.

All that computers could offer was evidence in favor of Fermat's Last Theorem. To the casual observer the evidence might seem to be overwhelming, but no amount of evidence is enough to satisfy mathematicians, a community of skeptics who will accept nothing other than absolute proof. Extrapolating a theory to cover an infinity of numbers based on evidence from a few numbers is a risky (and unacceptable) gamble.

One particular sequence of primes shows that extrapolation is a dangerous crutch upon which to rely. In the seventeenth century mathematicians showed by detailed examination that the following numbers are all prime:

31; 331; 3,331; 33,331; 333,331; 3,333,331; 33,333,331.

The next numbers in the sequence become increasingly giant, and checking whether or not they are also prime would have taken considerable effort. At the time some mathematicians were tempted to extrapolate from the pattern so far, and assume that all numbers of this form are prime. However, the next number in the pattern, 333,333,331, turned out not to be a prime:

$$333,333,331 = 17 \times 19,607,843.$$

Another good example that demonstrates why mathematicians refused to be persuaded by a few examples or the evidence from computers is the case of Euler's conjecture. Euler claimed that there were no solutions to an equation not dissimilar to Fermat's equation:

$$x^4 + y^4 + z^4 = w^4.$$

For two hundred years nobody could prove Euler's conjecture, but on the other hand nobody could disprove it by finding a counterexample. First manual searches and then years of computer sifting failed to find a solution. Lack of a counterexample was strong evidence in favor of the conjecture. Then, in 1988, Naom Elkies of Harvard University discovered the following solution:

$$2,682,440^4 + 15,365,639^4 + 18,796,760^4 = 20,615,673^4.$$

Despite all the evidence, Euler's conjecture turned out to be false. In fact Elkies proved that there were infinitely many solutions to the equation. The moral is that you cannot use evidence from the first million numbers to prove a conjecture about all numbers.

But the deceptive nature of Euler's conjecture is nothing compared to the *overestimated prime conjecture*. By scouring through larger and larger regimes of numbers, it becomes clear that the prime numbers become harder and harder to find. For instance, between 0 and 100 there are 25 primes but between 10,000,000 and 10,000,100 there are only 2 prime numbers. In 1791, when he was just fourteen years old, Carl Gauss predicted the approximate manner in which the frequency of prime numbers among all the other numbers would diminish. The formula was reasonably accurate but always seemed slightly to overestimate the true distribution of primes. Testing for primes up to a million, a billion, or a trillion would always show that Gauss's formula was marginally too generous and mathematicians were strongly tempted to believe that this would hold true for all numbers up to infinity, and thus was born the overestimated prime conjecture.

Then, in 1914, J. E. Littlewood, G. H. Hardy's collaborator at Cambridge, proved that in a sufficiently large regime Gauss's formula would *underestimate* the number of primes. In 1955 S. Skewes showed that the underestimate would occur sometime before reaching the number

$$10^{10^{10,000,000,000,000,000,000,000,000,000,000,000}}$$

This is a number beyond the imagination, and beyond any practical application. Hardy called Skewes's number "the largest number that has ever served any definite purpose in mathematics." He calculated that if one played chess with all the particles in the universe (10^{87}), where a move meant simply interchanging any two particles, then the number of possible games was roughly Skewes's number.

There was no reason why Fermat's Last Theorem should not turn out to be as cruel and deceptive as Euler's conjecture or the overestimated prime conjecture.

The Graduate

In 1975 Andrew Wiles began his career as a graduate student at Cambridge University. Over the next three years he was to work on his Ph.D. thesis and in that way serve his mathematical apprenticeship. Each student was guided and nurtured by a supervisor, and in Wiles's case that was the Australian John Coates, a professor at Emmanuel College, originally from Possum Brush, New South Wales.

Coates still recalls how he adopted Wiles: "I remember a colleague told me that he had a very good student who was just finishing part III of the mathematical tripos, and he urged me to take him as a student. I was very fortunate to have Andrew as a student. Even as a research student he had very deep ideas and it was always clear that he was a mathematician who would do great things. Of course, at that stage there was no question of any research student starting work directly on Fermat's Last Theorem. It was too difficult even for a thoroughly experienced mathematician."

For the past decade everything Wiles had done was directed toward preparing himself to meet Fermat's challenge, but now that he had joined the ranks of the professional mathematicians he had to be more pragmatic. He remembers how he had to temporarily surrender his dream: "When I went to Cambridge I

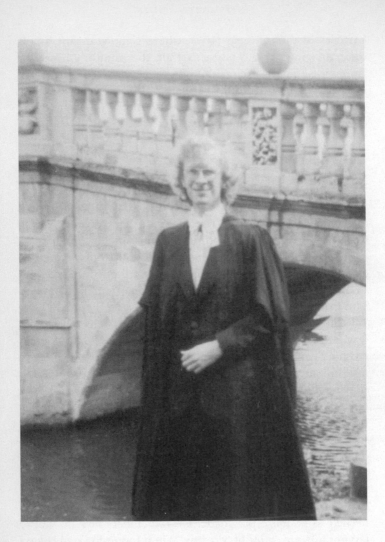

Andrew Wiles during his college years.

really put aside Fermat. It's not that I forgot about it — it was always there — but I realized that the only techniques we had to tackle it had been around for 130 years. It didn't seem that these techniques were really getting to the root of the problem. The risk with working on Fermat was that you could spend years getting nowhere. It's fine to work on any problem, so long as it generates interesting mathematics along the way — even if you don't solve it at the end of the day. The definition of a good mathematical problem is the mathematics it generates rather than the problem itself."

It was John Coates's responsibility to find Andrew a new obsession, something that would occupy his research for at least the next three years. "I think all a research supervisor can do for a student is try and push him in a fruitful direction. Of course, it's impossible to be sure what is a fruitful direction in terms of research but perhaps one thing that an older mathematician can do is use his horse sense, his intuition of what is a good area, and then it's really up to the student as to how far he can go in that direction." In the end Coates decided that Wiles should study an area of mathematics known as *elliptic curves*. This decision would eventually prove to be a turning point in Wiles's career and give him the techniques he would require for a new approach to tackling Fermat's Last Theorem.

The name "elliptic curves" is somewhat misleading, for they are neither ellipses nor even curved in the normal sense of the word. Rather, they are any equations that have the form

$y^2 = x^3 + ax^2 + bx + c,$ where a, b, c are any whole numbers.

They got their name because in the past they were used to measure the perimeters of ellipses and the lengths of planetary orbits, but for clarity I will simply refer to them as *elliptic equations* rather than elliptic curves.

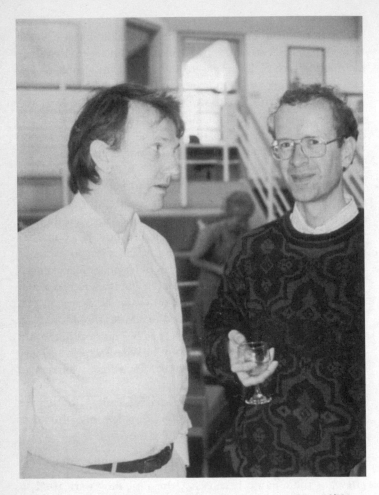

John Coates, Wiles's faculty supervisor in the 1970s, seen here in 1993 with his former student.

The challenge with elliptic equations, as with Fermat's Last Theorem, is to figure out if they have whole number solutions, and, if so, how many. For example, the elliptic equation

$$y^2 = x^3 - 2, \text{ where } a = 0, \ b = 0, \ c = -2,$$

has only one set of whole number solutions, namely

$$5^2 = 3^3 - 2, \text{ or } 25 = 27 - 2.$$

What makes elliptic equations particularly fascinating is that they occupy a curious niche between other, simpler equations that are almost trivial and other, more complicated equations that are impossible to solve. By simply changing the values of a, b, and c in the general elliptic equation mathematicians can generate an infinite variety of equations, each one with its own characteristics, but all of them just within the realm of solubility.

Elliptic equations were originally studied by the ancient Greek mathematicians, including Diophantus, who devoted large parts of his *Arithmetica* to exploring their properties. Probably inspired by Diophantus, Fermat also took up the challenge of elliptic equations, and, because they had been studied by his hero, Wiles was happy to explore them further. Even after two thousand years elliptic equations still offered formidable problems for students such as Wiles: "They are very far from being completely understood. There are many apparently simple questions I could pose on elliptic equations that are still unresolved. Even questions that Fermat himself considered are still unresolved. In some way all the mathematics that I've done can trace its ancestry to Fermat, if not Fermat's Last Theorem."

In the equations that Wiles studied as a graduate student, determining the exact number of solutions was so difficult that the only way to make any progress was to simplify the problem.

Figure 13. Conventional arithmetic can be thought of as
movements up and down the number line.

For example, the following elliptic equation is almost impossible
to tackle directly:

$$x^3 - x^2 = y^2 + y.$$

The challenge is to figure out how many whole number solutions
there are to the equation. One fairly trivial solution is $x = 0$ and $y = 0$:

$$0^3 - 0^2 = 0^2 + 0.$$

A slightly more interesting solution is $x = 1$ and $y = 0$:

$$1^3 - 1^2 = 0^2 + 0.$$

There may be other solutions but, with an infinite quantity of
whole numbers to investigate, giving a complete list of solutions
to this particular equation is an impossible task. A simpler task is
to look for solutions within a finite number space, so-called
clock arithmetic.

Earlier we saw how numbers can be thought of as marks along
the number line that extends to infinity, as shown in Figure 13.
To make the number space finite, clock arithmetic involves trun-
cating the line and looping it back on itself to form a number
ring as opposed to a number line. Figure 14 shows a 5-clock,
where the number line has been truncated at 5 and looped back
to 0. The number 5 vanishes and becomes equivalent to 0, and
therefore the only numbers in 5-clock arithmetic are 0, 1, 2, 3, 4.

Figure 14. In 5-clock arithmetic the number line is truncated at 5 and looped back on itself. The number 5 coincides with 0, and therefore is replaced by it.

In normal arithmetic we can think of addition as moving along the line a certain number of spaces. For example, 4 + 2 = 6 is the same as saying: begin at 4, and move along the number line 2 spaces, and arrive at 6.

However, in 5-clock arithmetic:

$$4 + 2 = 1.$$

This is because if we start at 4 and move around 2 spaces then we arrive back at 1. Clock arithmetic might appear unfamiliar, but in fact, as the name suggests, it is used every day when people discuss the time. Four hours after 11 o'clock (that is to say, 11 + 4) is generally not called 15 o'clock, but rather 3 o'clock. This is 12-clock arithmetic.

Because clock arithmetics deal with only a limited number space, it is relatively easy to work out all the possible solutions to an elliptic equation for a given clock arithmetic. For example, working in 5-clock arithmetic it is possible to list all the possible solutions to the elliptic equation

$$x^3 - x^2 = y^2 + y.$$

The solutions are:

$$x = 0, \quad y = 0,$$
$$x = 0, \quad y = 4,$$
$$x = 1, \quad y = 0,$$
$$x = 1, \quad y = 4.$$

Although some of these solutions would not be valid in normal arithmetic, in 5-clock arithmetic they are acceptable. For example, the fourth solution ($x = 1$, $y = 4$) works as follows:

$$x^3 - x^2 = y^2 + y$$
$$1^3 - 1^2 = 4^2 + 4$$
$$1 - 1 = 16 + 4$$
$$0 = 20.$$

In 5-clock arithmetic, 20 is equivalent to 0 because
5 will divide into 20 with a remainder of 0.

Because they could not list all the solutions to an elliptic equation working in infinite space, mathematicians, including Wiles, settled for working out the number of solutions in all the different clock arithmetics. For the elliptic equation given above, the number of solutions in 5-clock arithmetic is four, and so mathematicians say $E_5 = 4$. The number of solutions in other clock arithmetics can also be calculated. For example, in 7-clock arithmetic the number of solutions is nine, and so $E_7 = 9$.

To summarize their results, mathematicians list the number of solutions in each clock arithmetic and call this list the L-series for the elliptic equation. What the L stands for has been long forgotten, although some have suggested that it is the L of Gustav Lejeune-Dirichlet, who worked on elliptic equations. For clarity I will use the term E-series — the series that is derived from an elliptic equation. Here is an elliptic equation with its E-series:

Elliptic equation: $x^3 - x^2 = y^2 + y$

E-series: $E_1 = 1,$
$E_2 = 4,$
$E_3 = 4,$
$E_4 = 8,$
$E_5 = 4,$
$E_6 = 16,$
$E_7 = 9,$
$E_8 = 16,$
$\vdots$

Because mathematicians cannot say how many solutions some elliptic equations have in normal number space that extends up to infinity, the E-series appears to be next best thing. In fact the E-series encapsulates a great deal of information about the elliptic equation it describes. In the same way that biological DNA carries all the information required to construct a living organism, the E-series carries the essence of the elliptic equation. The hope was that by studying the E-series, this mathematical DNA, mathematicians would ultimately be able to calculate everything they could ever wish to know about an elliptic equation.

Working alongside John Coates, Wiles rapidly established his reputation as a brilliant number theorist with a profound understanding of elliptic equations and their E-series. As each new result was achieved and each paper published, Wiles did not realize that he was gathering the experience that would many years later bring him to the verge of a proof for Fermat's Last Theorem.

Although nobody was aware of it at the time, the mathematicians of postwar Japan had already triggered a chain of events which would inextricably link elliptic equations to Fermat's Last Theorem. By encouraging Wiles to study elliptic equations, Coates had given him the tools that would later enable him to work on his dream.

Yutaka Taniyama

5

Proof by Contradiction

The mathematician's patterns, like the painter's or the
poet's, must be beautiful; the ideas, like the colors or the
words, must fit together in a harmonious way. Beauty is
the first test: there is no permanent place in the world
for ugly mathematics.

G. H. Hardy

In January of 1954 a talented young mathematician at the University of Tokyo paid a routine visit to his departmental library. Goro Shimura was in search of a copy of *Mathematische Annalen*, Vol. 24. In particular he was after a paper by Deuring on the algebraic theory of complex multiplication, which he needed in order to help him with a particularly awkward and esoteric calculation.

To his surprise and dismay, the volume was already out. The borrower was Yutaka Taniyama, a vague acquaintance of Shimura who lived on the other side of the campus. Shimura wrote to Taniyama explaining that he urgently needed the journal to complete the nasty calculation, and politely asked when it would be returned.

A few days later, a postcard landed on Shimura's desk. Taniyama had replied, saying that he too was working on the exact same calculation and was stuck at the same point in the logic. He suggested that they share their ideas and perhaps col-

Goro Shimura

laborate on the problem. This chance encounter over a library book ignited a partnership that would change the course of mathematical history.

Taniyama was born on November 12, 1927, in a small town a few miles north of Tokyo. The Japanese character symbolizing his first name was intended to read "Toyo," but most people outside his family misinterpreted it as "Yutaka," and as Taniyama grew up he accepted and adopted this title. As a child Taniyama's education was constantly interrupted. He suffered several bouts of ill health, and during his teenage years he was struck down by tuberculosis and had to miss two years of high school. The onset of war caused even greater disruption to his schooling.

Goro Shimura, one year younger than Taniyama, had his education stopped altogether during the war years. His school was shut down and, instead of attending lessons, Shimura had to help the war effort by working in a factory assembling aircraft parts. Each evening he would attempt to make up for his lost schooling, and in particular found himself drawn to mathematics. "Of course there are many subjects to learn, but mathematics was the easiest because I could simply read mathematical textbooks. I learnt calculus by reading books. If I'd wanted to pursue chemistry or physics then I would have needed scientific equipment and I had no access to such things. I never thought that I was talented. I was just curious."

A few years after the war had finished, Shimura and Taniyama found themselves at university. By the time they had exchanged postcards over the library book, life in Tokyo was beginning to return to normal and the two young academics could afford one or two small luxuries. They spent their afternoons in the coffee shops, in the evenings they dined in a little restaurant specializing in whale meat, and weekends they would stroll through the botanical gardens or the city park. All ideal locations for discussing their latest mathematical thoughts.

Although Shimura had a whimsical streak — even today he retains his fondness for Zen jokes — he was far more conservative and conventional than his intellectual partner. Shimura would rise at dawn and immediately get down to work, whereas his colleague would often still be awake at this time, having worked through the night. Visitors to his apartment would often find Taniyama fast asleep in the middle of the afternoon.

While Shimura was fastidious, Taniyama was sloppy to the point of laziness. Surprisingly this was a trait that Shimura admired: "He was gifted with the special capability of making many mistakes, mostly in the right direction. I envied him for this and tried in vain to imitate him, but found it quite difficult to make good mistakes."

Taniyama was the epitome of the absentminded genius, and this was reflected in his appearance. He was incapable of tying a decent knot, and so he decided that rather than tie his shoelaces a dozen times a day he would not tie them at all. He would always wear the same peculiar green suit with a strange metallic sheen. It was made from a fabric that was so outrageous that it had been rejected by the other members of his family.

When they met in 1954 Taniyama and Shimura were just beginning their mathematical careers. The tradition was, and still is, for young researchers to be taken under the wing of a professor who would guide the fledgling brain, but Taniyama and Shimura rejected this form of apprenticeship. During the war real research had ground to a halt, and even by the 1950s the mathematics faculty had still not recovered. According to Shimura, the professors were "tired, jaded and disillusioned." In comparison the post-war students were passionate and eager to learn, and they soon realized that the only way forward would be for them to teach themselves. The students organized regular seminars, taking it in turn to inform each other of the latest techniques and break-throughs. Despite his otherwise lackadaisical attitude, when it came to the seminars Taniyama provided a ferocious driving force. He would encourage the more senior students to explore uncharted territory, and for the younger students he acted as a father figure.

Because the students were isolated from the West, the seminars would occasionally cover subjects that were generally considered passé in Europe and America. One particularly unfashionable topic that fascinated both Taniyama and Shimura was the study of *modular forms.*

Modular forms are some of the most bizarre and wonderful objects in mathematics. They are one of the most esoteric entities in mathematics, and yet the twentieth-century number theorist Martin Eichler rated them as one of the five fundamental opera-tions: addition, subtraction, multiplication, division, and modular forms. Most mathematicians would consider themselves masters of the first four operations, but the fifth one they still find a little confusing.

The key feature of modular forms is their inordinate level of symmetry. Although most people are familiar with the everyday concept of symmetry, it has a very particular meaning in math-ematics, which is that an object has symmetry if it can be trans-formed in a particular way and yet afterward appear to be unchanged. To appreciate the immense symmetry of a modular form it helps to first examine the symmetry of a more mundane object such as a simple square.

Figure 15. A simple square exhibits both rotational and reflectional symmetry.

In the case of a square, one form of symmetry is rotational. That is to say, if we imagine a pivot at the point where the x-axis and y-axis cross, then the square in Figure 15 can be rotated by one quarter of a turn, and afterward it will appear to be unchanged. Similarly, rotations by half a turn, three-quarters of a turn, and one full turn will also leave the square apparently unchanged.

In addition to rotational symmetry the square also possesses reflectional symmetry. If we imagine a mirror placed along the x-axis then the top half of the square would reflect exactly onto the lower half, and vice versa, so after the transformation the square would appear to remain unchanged. Similarly we can define three other mirrors (along the y-axis and along the two diagonals) for which the reflected square would appear to be identical to the original one.

The simple square is relatively symmetric, possessing both rotational and reflectional symmetries, but it does not possess any translational symmetry. This means that if the square were to be shifted in any direction, an observer would spot the movement

Figure 16. An infinite surface tiled with squares exhibits rotational and reflectional symmetry, and in addition has translational symmetry.

immediately because its position relative to the axes would have changed. However, if the whole of the space were tiled with squares, as shown in Figure 16, this infinite collection of squares would then have translational symmetry. If the infinite tiled surface were to be shifted up or down by one or more tile spaces, then the translated tiling would appear to be identical to the original one. Furthermore, the tiled surface still possesses rotational and reflectional symmetry.

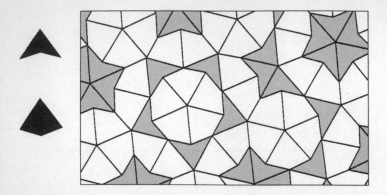

Figure 17. By using two different tiles, the kite and the dart, Roger Penrose was able to cover a surface. However, Penrose tiling does not possess translational symmetry.

The symmetry of tiled surfaces is a relatively straightforward idea, but as with other seemingly simple concepts there are many subtleties hidden within it. For example, in the 1970s the British physicist and recreational mathematician Roger Penrose began dabbling with different tiles on the same surface. Eventually he identified two particularly interesting shapes, called the kite and the dart, which are shown in Figure 17. On their own each of these shapes could not be used to tile a surface without leaving gaps or overlaps, but together they could be used to create a rich set of tiling patterns. The kites and darts can be fitted together in an infinite number of ways, and although each pattern is apparently similar, they all vary in detail. One pattern made from kites and darts is shown in Figure 17.

Another remarkable feature of Penrose tilings (the patterns generated by tiles such as the kite and dart) is that they can exhibit a very restricted level of symmetry. At first sight it would appear that the tiling shown in Figure 17 would have translational symmetry, and yet any attempt to shift the pattern across so that it effectively remains unchanged ends in failure. Penrose tilings are deceptively unsymmetrical, and this is why they fascinate mathematicians and have become the starting point for a whole new area of mathematics.

While the fascinating thing about Penrose's tiled surfaces is their restricted symmetry, the interesting property of modular forms is that they exhibit infinite symmetry. The modular forms studied by Taniyama and Shimura can be shifted, switched, swapped, reflected, and rotated in an infinite number of ways and still they remain unchanged, making them the most symmetrical of mathematical objects.

Unfortunately, drawing, or even imagining, a modular form is impossible. In the case of the square tiling we have an object that lives in two dimensions, its space being defined by the x-axis and the y-axis. A modular form is also defined by two axes, but the axes are both complex, i.e., each axis has a real and an imaginary part and effectively becomes two axes. Therefore the first complex axis must be represented by two axes, x_r-axis (real) and x_i-axis (imaginary), and the second complex axis is represented by two axes, y_r-axis (real) and y_i-axis (imaginary). To be precise, modular forms live in the upper half-plane of this complex space, but what is most important to appreciate is that this is a four-dimensional space (x_r, x_i, y_r, y_i).

This four-dimensional space is called *hyperbolic space*. The hyperbolic universe is tricky to comprehend for humans, who are constrained to living in a conventional three-dimensional world, but four-dimensional space is a mathematically valid concept, and it is this extra dimension that gives the modular forms such an immensely high level of symmetry. The artist

Figure 18. Mauritz Escher's *Circle Limit IV* conveys some of the symmetry of modular forms.

Mauritz Escher was fascinated by mathematical ideas and attempted to convey the concept of hyperbolic space in some of his etchings and paintings. Figure 18 shows Escher's *Circle Limit IV*, which embeds the hyperbolic world into the two-dimensional page. In true hyperbolic space the bats and angels would be the same size, and the repetition is indicative of the high level of symmetry. Although some of this symmetry can be seen on the two-dimensional page, there is an increasing distortion toward the edge of the picture.

The modular forms that live in hyperbolic space come in various shapes and sizes, but each one is built from the same basic ingredients. What differentiates each modular form is the amount of each ingredient it contains. The ingredients of a modular form are labeled from one to infinity (M_1, M_2, M_3, M_4, …) and so a particular modular form might contain one lot of ingredient one ($M_1 = 1$), three lots of ingredient two ($M_2 = 3$), two lots of ingredient three ($M_3 = 2$), etc. This information describing how a modular form is constructed can be summarized in a so-called modular series, or M-series, a list of the ingredients and the quantity of each one required:

$$M\text{-series:} \quad \begin{aligned} M_1 &= 1, \\ M_2 &= 3, \\ M_3 &= 2. \\ &\vdots \end{aligned}$$

Just as the E-series is the DNA for elliptic equations, the M-series is the DNA for modular forms. The amount of each ingredient listed in the M-series is critical. Depending on how you change the amount of, say, the first ingredient you might generate a completely different, but equally symmetrical, modular form, or you might destroy the symmetry altogether and generate a new object that is not a modular form. If the quantity of each ingredient is arbitrarily chosen, then the result will probably be an object with little or no symmetry.

Modular forms stand very much on their own within mathematics. In particular, they would seem to be completely unrelated to the subject that Wiles would study at Cambridge, elliptic equations. The modular form is an enormously complicated beast, studied largely because of its symmetry and discovered only in the nineteenth century. The elliptic equation dates back to the ancient Greeks and has nothing to do with symmetry. Modular forms and elliptic equations live in completely different regions of the mathematical cosmos, and nobody would ever have believed that there was the remotest link between the two subjects. However, Taniyama and Shimura were to shock the mathematical community by suggesting that elliptic equations and modular forms were effectively one and the same thing. According to these two maverick mathematicians, they could unify the modular and elliptic worlds.

Wishful Thinking

In September 1955 an international symposium was held in Tokyo. It was a unique opportunity for the many young Japanese researchers to show off to the rest of the world what they had learned. They handed around a collection of thirty-six problems related to their work, accompanied by a humble introduction — *Some unsolved problems in mathematics: no mature preparation has been made, so there may be some trivial or already solved ones among these. The participants are requested to give comments on any of these problems.*

Four of the questions were from Taniyama, and these hinted at a curious relationship between modular forms and elliptic equations. These innocent questions would ultimately lead to a revolution in number theory. Taniyama had looked at the first few terms in the *M*-series of a particular modular form. He

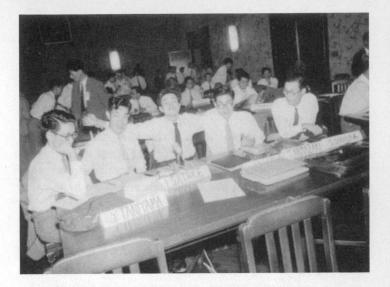

In 1955 Goro Shimura and Yutaka Taniyama attended an international symposium in Tokyo.

recognized the pattern and realized that it was identical to the list of numbers in the *E*-series of a well-known elliptic equation. He calculated a few more terms in each series, and still the *M*-series of the modular form and *E*-series of the elliptic equation matched perfectly.

This was an astonishing discovery because, for no apparent reason, this modular form could be related to an elliptic equation through their respective *M*-series and *E*-series — these series were identical. The mathematical DNA that made up these two entities was exactly the same. This was a doubly profound discovery. First, it suggested that deep down there was a fundamental relationship between the modular form and the elliptic equation, objects that come from opposite ends of mathematics. Second, it meant that mathematicians, who already knew the M-series for the modular form, would not have to calculate the E-series for the corresponding elliptic equation because it would be the same as the M-series.

Relationships between apparently different subjects are as creatively important in mathematics as they are in any discipline. The relationship hints at some underlying truth that enriches both subjects. For instance, originally scientists had studied electricity and magnetism as two completely separate phenomena. Then, in the nineteenth century, theorists and experimentalists realized that electricity and magnetism were intimately related. This resulted in a deeper understanding of both of them. Electric currents generate magnetic fields, and magnets can induce electricity in wires passing close to them. This led to the invention of dynamos and electric motors, and ultimately the discovery that light itself is the result of magnetic and electric fields oscillating in harmony.

Taniyama examined a few other modular forms and in each case the M-series seemed to correspond perfectly with the E-series of an elliptic equation. He began to wonder if it could be that every single modular form could be matched with an elliptic equation. Perhaps every modular form has the same DNA as an elliptic equation: Perhaps each modular form is an elliptic equation in disguise? The questions he handed out at the symposium were related to this hypothesis.

The idea that every elliptic equation was related to a modular form was so extraordinary that those who glanced at Taniyama's questions treated them as nothing more than a curious observation. Sure enough, Taniyama had demonstrated that a few elliptic equations could be related to particular modular forms, but they claimed that this was nothing more than a coincidence. According to the skeptics, Taniyama's claim of a more general and universal relationship seemed to be largely unsubstantiated. The hypothesis was based on intuition rather than on any real evidence.

Taniyama's only ally was Shimura, who believed in the power and depth of his friend's idea. Following the symposium he worked with Taniyama in an attempt to develop the hypothesis to a level where the rest of the world could no longer ignore their work. Shimura wanted to find more evidence to back up the relationship between the modular and elliptic worlds. The collaboration was temporarily halted when in 1957 Shimura was invited to attend the Institute for Advanced Study in Princeton. Following his two years as a visiting professor in America he intended to resume working with Taniyama, but this was never to happen. On November 17, 1958, Yutaka Taniyama committed suicide.

Death of a Genius

Shimura still keeps the postcard that Taniyama sent him when they first made contact over the library book. He also keeps the last letter Taniyama wrote to him while he was away in Princeton, but it contains not the merest hint as to what would happen just two months later. To this day Shimura has no understanding of what was behind Taniyama's suicide. "I was very much puzzled. Puzzlement may be the best word. Of course I was sad, but it was so sudden. I got his letter in September and he died in early November, and I was unable to make sense out of this. Of course, later I heard various things and I tried to reconcile myself with his death. Some people said that he lost confidence in himself but not mathematically."

What was particularly confusing for Taniyama's friends was that he had just fallen in love with Misako Suzuki and planned to marry her later that year. In a personal tribute published in the *Bulletin of the London Mathematical Society*, Goro Shimura recollects Taniyama's engagement to Misako and the weeks that led up to his suicide:

> When informed of their engagement, I was somewhat surprised, since I had vaguely thought she was not his type, but I felt no misgivings. I was told afterward that they had signed a lease for an apartment, apparently a better one, for their new home, had bought some kitchenware together, and had been preparing for their wedding. Everything looked promising for them and their friends. Then the catastrophe befell them.
>
> On the morning of Monday, November 17, 1958, the superintendent of his apartment found him dead in his room with a note left on a desk. It was written on three pages of a notebook of the type he had been using for his scholastic work; its first paragraph read like this:

> Until yesterday, I had no definite intention of killing myself. But more than a few must have noticed that lately I have been tired both physically and mentally. As to the cause of my suicide, I don't quite understand it myself, but it is not the result of a particular incident, nor of a specific matter. Merely may I say, I am in the frame of mind that I lost confidence in my future. There may be someone to whom my suicide will be troubling or a blow to a certain degree. I

sincerely hope that this incident will cast no dark shadow over the future of that person. At any rate, I cannot deny that this is a kind of betrayal, but please excuse it as my last act in my own way, as I have been doing my own way all my life.

He went on to describe, quite methodically, his wish of how his belongings should be disposed of, and which books and records were the ones he had borrowed from the library or from his friends, and so on. Specifically he says: "I would like to leave the records and the player to Misako Suzuki provided she will not be upset by me leaving them to her." Also he explains how far he reached in the undergraduate courses on calculus and linear algebra he was teaching, and concludes the note with an apology to his colleagues for the inconveniences this act could cause.

Thus one of the most brilliant and pioneering minds of the time ended his life by his own will. He had attained the age of thirty-one only five days earlier.

A few weeks after the suicide, tragedy struck a second time. His fiancée, Misako Suzuki, also took her own life. She reportedly left a note that read: "We promised each other that no matter where we went, we would never be separated. Now that he is gone, I must go too in order to join him."

Philosophy of Goodness

During his short career Taniyama contributed many radical ideas to mathematics. The questions he handed out at the symposium contained his greatest insight, but it was so ahead of its time that he would never live to see its enormous influence on number theory. His intellectual creativity was to be sadly missed, along with his guiding role within the community of young Japanese scientists. Shimura clearly remembers Taniyama's influence: "He was always kind to his colleagues, especially to his juniors, and he genuinely cared about their welfare. He was the moral support of many of those who came into mathematical contact with him, including of course myself. Probably he was never conscious of this role he was playing. But I feel his noble generosity in this respect even more strongly now than when he was alive. And yet nobody was able to give him any support when he desperately needed it. Reflecting on this, I am overwhelmed by the bitterest grief."

Following Taniyama's death, Shimura concentrated all his efforts on understanding the exact relationship between elliptic equations and modular forms. As the years passed he struggled to gather more evidence and one or two pieces of logic to support the theory. Gradually he became increasingly convinced that every single elliptic equation must be related to a modular form. Other mathematicians were still dubious and Shimura recalls a conversation with an eminent colleague. The professor inquired, "I hear that you propose that some elliptic equations can be linked to modular forms."

"No, you don't understand," replied Shimura. "It's not just some elliptic equations, it's *every* elliptic equation!"

Shimura could not prove that this was the case, but every time he tested the hypothesis it seemed to be true, and in any case it all seemed to fit in with his broad mathematical philosophy. "I have this philosophy of goodness. Mathematics should contain goodness. So in the case of the elliptic equation, one might call the equation good if it is parameterized by a modular form. I expect all elliptic equations to be good. It's a rather crude philosophy but one can always take it as a starting point. Then, of course, I had to develop various technical reasons for the conjecture. I might say that the conjecture stemmed from that philosophy of goodness. Most mathematicians do mathematics from an aesthetic point of view and that philosophy of goodness comes from my aesthetic viewpoint."

Eventually Shimura's accumulation of evidence meant that his theory about elliptic equations and modular forms became more widely accepted. He could not prove to the rest of the world that it was true, but at least it was now more than mere wishful thinking. There was enough evidence for it to be worthy of the title of conjecture. Initially it was referred to as the Taniyama-Shimura conjecture in recognition of the man who inspired it and his colleague who went on to develop it fully.

In due course André Weil, one of the godfathers of twentieth-century number theory, was to adopt the conjecture and publicize it in the West. Weil investigated the idea of Shimura and Taniyama, and found even more solid evidence in favor of it. As a result, the hypothesis was often referred to as the Taniyama-Shimura-Weil conjecture, sometimes as the Taniyama-Weil conjecture, and occasionally as the Weil conjecture. In fact there has been much debate and controversy over the official naming of the conjecture. For those of you interested in combinatorics there are fifteen possible permutations given the three names involved, and it is quite probable that every one of those combinations has appeared in print over the years. However, I will refer to the conjecture by its original title, the Taniyama-Shimura conjecture.

Professor John Coates, who guided Andrew Wiles when he was a student, was himself a student when the Taniyama-Shimura conjecture became a talking point in the West. "I began research in 1966 when the conjecture of Taniyama and Shimura was sweeping through the world. Everyone was amazed and began to look seriously at the issue of whether all elliptic equations could be modular. This was a tremendously exciting time; the only problem, of course, was that it seemed very hard to make progress. I think it's fair to say that beautiful though this idea was it seemed very difficult to actually prove, and that's what we're primarily interested in as mathematicians."

During the late sixties hordes of mathematicians repeatedly tested the Taniyama-Shimura conjecture. Starting with an elliptic equation and its E-series, they would search for a modular form with an identical M-series. In every single case the elliptic equation did indeed have an associated modular form. Although this was good evidence in favor of the Taniyama-Shimura conjecture, it was by no means a proof. Mathematicians suspected that it was true, but until somebody could find a logical proof it would remain merely a conjecture.

Barry Mazur, a professor at Harvard University, witnessed the rise of the Taniyama-Shimura conjecture. "It was a wonderful conjecture — the surmise that every elliptic equation is associated with a modular form — but to begin with it was ignored because it was so ahead of its time. When it was first proposed it was not taken up because it was so astounding. On the one hand you have the elliptic world, and on the other you have the modular world. Both these branches of mathematics had been studied intensively but separately. Mathematicians studying elliptic equations might not be well versed in things modular, and conversely. Then along comes the Taniyama-Shimura conjecture, which is the grand surmise that there's a bridge between these two completely different worlds. Mathematicians love to build bridges."

The value of mathematical bridges is enormous. They enable communities of mathematicians who have been living on separate islands to exchange ideas and explore each other's creations. Mathematics consists of islands of knowledge in a sea of ignorance. For example, there is the island occupied by geometers who study shape and form, and then there is the island of probability where mathematicians discuss risk and chance. There are dozens of such islands, each one with its own unique language, incomprehensible to the inhabitants of other islands. The language of geometry is quite different from the language of probability, and the slang of calculus is meaningless to those who speak only statistics.

The great potential of the Taniyama-Shimura conjecture was that it would connect two islands and allow them to speak to each other for the first time. Barry Mazur thinks of the Taniyama-Shimura conjecture as a translating device similar to the Rosetta stone, which contained Egyptian demotic, ancient Greek, and hieroglyphics. Because demotic and Greek were already understood, archaeologists could decipher hieroglyphics for the first time. "It's as if you know one language and this Rosetta stone is going to give you an intense understanding of the other language," says Mazur. "But the Taniyama-Shimura conjecture is a Rosetta stone with a certain magical power. The conjecture has the very pleasant feature that simple intuitions in the modular world translate into deep truths in the elliptic world, and conversely. What's more, very profound problems in the elliptic world can get solved sometimes by translating them using this Rosetta stone into the modular world, and discovering that we have the insights and tools in the modular world to treat the translated problem. Back in the elliptic world we would have been at a loss."

If the Taniyama-Shimura conjecture was true it would enable mathematicians to tackle elliptic problems that had remained unsolved for centuries by approaching them through the modular world. The hope was that the fields of elliptic equations and modular forms could be unified. The conjecture also inspired the hope that links might exist between various other mathematical subjects.

During the 1960s Robert Langlands, at the Institute for Advanced Study, Princeton, was struck by the potency of the Taniyama-Shimura conjecture. Even though the conjecture had not been proved, Langlands believed that it was just one element of a much grander scheme of unification. He was confident that there were links between all the main mathematical topics and began to look for these unifications. Within a few years a number of links began to emerge. All these other unification conjectures were much weaker and more speculative than Taniyama-Shimura, but they formed an intricate network of hypothetical bridges between many areas of mathematics. Langlands's dream was to see each of these conjectures proved one by one, leading to a grand unified mathematics.

Langlands discussed his plan for the future and tried to persuade other mathematicians to take part in what became known as the Langlands program, a concerted effort to prove his myriad of conjectures. There seemed to be no obvious way to prove such speculative links, but if the dream could be made a reality then the reward would be enormous. Any insoluble problem in one area of mathematics could be transformed into an analogous problem in another area, where a whole new arsenal of techniques could be brought to bear on it. If a solution was still elusive, the problem could be transformed and transported to yet another area of mathematics, and so on, until it was solved. One day, according to the Langlands program, mathematicians would be able to solve their most esoteric and intractable problems by shuffling them around the mathematical landscape.

There were also important implications for the applied sciences and engineering. Whether it is modeling the interactions between colliding quarks or discovering the most efficient way to organize a telecommunications network, often the key to the problem is performing a mathematical calculation. In some areas of science and technology the complexity of the calculations is so immense that they cannot be completed, and consequently progress in those subjects has been severely hindered. If only mathematicians could prove the linking conjectures of the Langlands program, then there would be shortcuts to solving real-world problems, as well as abstract ones.

By the 1970s the Langlands program had become a blueprint for the future of mathematics, but this route to a problem-solver's paradise was blocked by the simple fact that nobody had any real idea how to prove any of Langlands's conjectures. The strongest conjecture within the program was still Taniyama-Shimura, but even this seemed out of reach. A proof of the Taniyama-Shimura conjecture would be the first step in the Langlands program, and as such it had become one of the biggest prizes in modern number theory.

Despite its status as an unproven conjecture, Taniyama-Shimura was still mentioned in hundreds of mathematical research papers speculating about what would happen if it could be proved. The papers would begin by clearly stating the caveat "Assuming that the Taniyama-Shimura conjecture is true . . . ," and then they would continue to outline a solution for some unsolved problem. Of course, these results could themselves only be hypothetical, because they relied on the Taniyama-Shimura conjecture being true. These new hypothetical results were in turn incorporated into other results until there existed a plethora of mathematics that relied on the truth of the Taniyama-Shimura conjecture. This one conjecture was a foundation for a whole new architecture of mathematics, but until it could be proved the whole structure was vulnerable.

At the time, Andrew Wiles was a young researcher at Cambridge University, and he recalls the trepidation that plagued the mathematics community in the 1970s: "We built more and more conjectures which stretched further and further into the future, but they would all be ridiculous if the Taniyama-Shimura conjecture was not true. So we had to prove Taniyama-Shimura to show that this whole design we had hopefully mapped out for the future was correct."

Mathematicians had constructed a fragile house of cards. They dreamed that one day someone would give their architecture the solid foundation it needed. They also had to live with the nightmare that one day someone might prove that Taniyama and Shimura were in fact wrong, causing two decades' worth of research to crash to the ground.

The Missing Link

During the autumn of 1984 a select group of number theorists gathered for a symposium in Oberwolfach, a small town in the heart of Germany's Black Forest. They had been brought together to discuss various breakthroughs in the study of elliptic equations, and naturally some of the speakers would occasionally report any minor progress that they had made toward proving the Taniyama-Shimura conjecture. One of the speakers,

Gerhard Frey, a mathematician from Saarbrücken, could not offer any new ideas as to how to attack the conjecture, but he did make the remarkable claim that if anyone could prove the Taniyama-Shimura conjecture then they would also immediately prove Fermat's Last Theorem.

When Frey got up to speak he began by writing down Fermat's equation:

$$x^n + y^n = z^n \text{ where } n \text{ is greater than 2.}$$

Fermat's Last Theorem claims that there are no whole number solutions to this equation, but Frey explored what would happen if the Last Theorem were false, i.e., that there is at least one solution. Frey had no idea what his hypothetical, and heretical, solution might be and so he labeled the unknown numbers with the letters A, B, and C:

$$A^N + B^N = C^N.$$

Frey then proceeded to "rearrange" the equation. This is a rigorous mathematical procedure that changes the appearance of the equation without altering its integrity. By a deft series of complicated maneuvers Frey fashioned Fermat's original equation, with the hypothetical solution, into

$$y^2 = x^3 + (A^N - B^N)x^2 - A^N B^N.$$

Although this rearrangement seems very different from the original equation, it is a direct consequence of the hypothetical solution. That is to say if, and it is a big "if," there is a solution to Fermat's equation and Fermat's Last Theorem is false, then this rearranged equation must also exist. Initially Frey's audience was not particularly impressed by his rearrangement, but then he pointed out that this new equation was in fact an elliptic equation, albeit a rather convoluted and exotic one. Elliptic equations have the form

$$y^2 = x^3 + ax^2 + bx + c,$$

but if we let

$$a = A^N - B^N, \quad b = 0, \quad c = -A^N B^N,$$

then it is easier to appreciate the elliptical nature of Frey's equation.

By turning Fermat's equation into an elliptic equation, Frey had linked Fermat's Last Theorem to the Taniyama-Shimura conjecture. Frey then pointed out to his audience that his elliptic equation, created from the solution to the Fermat equation, is truly bizarre. In fact, Frey claimed that his elliptic equation is so weird that the repercussions of its existence would be devastating for the Taniyama-Shimura conjecture.

When Frey called his elliptic equation "weird," this was his way of expressing the unique nature of its E-series. The E-series contained such a strange sequence of numbers that it would be inconceivable for a modular form to have an identical M-series. Hence it was said that Frey's elliptical equation could not be modular.

Remember that Frey's elliptic equation is only a phantom equation. Its existence is conditional on Fermat's Last Theorem being false. However, if Frey's elliptic equation does exist, then it is so strange that it would be seemingly impossible for it ever to be related to a modular form. But the Taniyama-Shimura conjecture claims that *every* elliptic equation must be related to a modular form. Therefore the existence of Frey's weird elliptic equation defies the Taniyama-Shimura conjecture.

In other words, Frey's argument was as follows:

(1) If (and only if) Fermat's Last Theorem is wrong, then Frey's elliptic equation exists.
(2) Frey's elliptic equation is so weird that it can never be modular.
(3) The Taniyama-Shimura conjecture claims that every elliptic equation must be modular.
(4) Therefore the Taniyama-Shimura conjecture must be false!

Alternatively, and more importantly, Frey could run his argument backward:

(1) If the Taniyama-Shimura conjecture can be proved to be true, then every elliptic equation must be modular.
(2) If every elliptic equation must be modular, then the Frey elliptic equation is forbidden to exist.
(3) If the Frey elliptic equation does not exist, then there can be no solutions to Fermat's equation.
(4) Therefore Fermat's Last Theorem is true!

Gerhard Frey had come to the dramatic conclusion that the truth of Fermat's Last Theorem would be an immediate consequence of the Taniyama-Shimura conjecture being proved. Frey claimed that if mathematicians could prove the Taniyama-Shimura conjecture then they would automatically prove Fermat's Last Theorem. For the first time in a hundred years the world's hardest mathematical problem looked vulnerable. According to Frey, proving the Taniyama-Shimura conjecture was the only hurdle to proving Fermat's Last Theorem.

Although the audience was impressed by Frey's brilliant insight, they were also struck by an elementary blunder in his logic. Almost everyone in the auditorium, except Frey himself, had spotted it. The mistake did not appear to be serious; nonetheless, as it stood Frey's work was incomplete. Whoever could correct the error first would take the credit for linking Fermat and Taniyama-Shimura.

Frey's audience dashed out of the lecture theater and headed for the photocopying room. Often the importance of a talk can be gauged by the length of the queue waiting to run off copies of the lecture. Once they had a complete outline of Frey's ideas, they returned to their respective institutes and began to try to fill in the gap.

Frey's argument depended on the fact that his elliptic equation derived from Fermat's equation was so weird that it was not modular. His work was incomplete because he had not quite demonstrated that his elliptic equation was sufficiently weird. Only when somebody could prove the *absolute* weirdness of Frey's elliptic equation would a proof of the Taniyama-Shimura conjecture then imply a proof of Fermat's Last Theorem.

Initially mathematicians believed that proving the weirdness of Frey's elliptic equation would be a fairly routine process. At first sight Frey's mistake seemed to have been elementary and everyone who had been at Oberwolfach assumed that it was going to be a race to see who could the shuffle the algebra most quickly. The expectation was that somebody would send out an E-mail within a matter of days describing how they had established the true weirdness of Frey's elliptic equation.

A week passed and there was no such E-mail. Months passed and what was supposed to be a mathematical mad dash was turning into a marathon. It seemed that Fermat was still teasing and tormenting his descendants. Frey had outlined a tantalizing strategy for proving Fermat's Last Theorem, but even the first elementary step, proving that Frey's hypothetical elliptic equation was not modular, was baffling mathematicians around the globe.

To prove that an elliptic equation is not modular, mathematicians were looking for invariants similar to those described in Chapter 4. The knot invariant showed that one knot could not be transformed into another, and Loyd's puzzle invariant showed that his 14–15 puzzle could not be transformed into the correct arrangement. If number theorists could discover an appropriate invariant to describe Frey's elliptic equation, then they could prove that, no matter what was done to it, it could never be transformed into a modular form. In a way, the invariant would be a measure of weirdness.

One of those toiling to prove and complete the connection between the Taniyama-Shimura conjecture and Fermat's Last Theorem was Ken Ribet, a professor at the University of California at Berkeley. Since the lecture at Oberwolfach, Ribet had become obsessed with trying to prove that Frey's elliptic equation was too weird to be modular. After eighteen months of effort he, along with everybody else, was getting nowhere. Then, in the summer of 1986, Ribet's colleague Professor Barry Mazur was visiting Berkeley to attend the International Congress of Mathematicians. The two friends met up for a cappuccino at the Café Strada and began sharing bad luck stories and grumbling about the state of mathematics.

Eventually they started discussing the latest news on the various attempts to prove the weirdness of Frey's elliptic equation, and Ribet began explaining a tentative strategy that he had been exploring. The approach seemed vaguely promising, but he

Ken Ribet

could prove only a very minor part of it. "I sat down with Barry and told him what I was working on. I mentioned that I'd proved a very special case, but I didn't know what to do next to generalize it to get the full strength of the proof."

Professor Mazur sipped his cappuccino and listened to Ribet's idea. Then he stopped and stared at Ken in disbelief. "But don't you see? You've already done it! All you have to do is add some gamma-zero of (M) structure and just run through your argument and it works. It gives you everything you need."

Ribet looked at Mazur, looked at his cappuccino, and looked back at Mazur. It was the most important moment of Ribet's career, and he recalls it in loving detail. "I said you're absolutely right — of course — how did I not see this? I was completely astonished because it had never occurred to me to add the extra gamma-zero of (M) structure, simple as it sounds."

It should be noted that, although *adding gamma-zero of (M) structure* sounds simple to Ken Ribet, it is an esoteric step of logic that only a handful of the world's mathematicians could have concocted over a casual cappuccino.

"It was the crucial ingredient that I had been missing and it had been staring me in the face. I wandered back to my apartment on a cloud, thinking: My God, is this really correct? I was completely enthralled and I sat down and started scribbling on a pad of paper. After an hour or two I'd written everything out and verified that I knew the key steps and that it all fitted together. I ran through my argument and I said, yes, this absolutely has to work. And there were of course thousands of mathematicians at the International Congress and I sort of casually mentioned to a few people that I'd proved that the Taniyama-Shimura conjecture implies Fermat's Last Theorem. It spread like wildfire and soon large groups of people knew; they were running up to me asking,

Is it really true you've proved that Frey's elliptic equation is not modular?
And I had to think for a minute and all of a sudden I said, *Yes, I have.*"

Fermat's Last Theorem was now inextricably linked to the Taniyama-Shimura conjecture. If somebody could prove that every elliptic equation is modular, then this would imply that Fermat's equation had no solutions, and immediately prove Fermat's Last Theorem.

For three and half centuries Fermat's Last Theorem had been an isolated problem, a curious and impossible riddle on the edge of mathematics. Now Ken Ribet, inspired by Gerhard Frey, had brought it center stage. The most important problem from the seventeenth century was coupled to the most significant problem of the twentieth century. A puzzle of enormous historical and emotional importance was linked to a conjecture that could revolutionize modern mathematics.

In effect mathematicians could now attack Fermat's Last Theorem by adopting a strategy of proof by contradiction. To prove that the Last Theorem is true, mathematicians would begin by assuming it to be false, which would imply that the Taniyama-Shimura conjecture was false. However, if Taniyama-Shimura could be proven true, then this would be incompatible with Fermat's Last Theorem being false, and therefore the Last Theorem would have to be true. Frey had clearly defined the task ahead. Mathematicians would automatically prove the Last Theorem if they could first prove the Taniyama-Shimura conjecture.

Initially there was renewed hope, but then the reality of the situation dawned. Mathematicians had been trying to prove Taniyama-Shimura for thirty years and they had failed. Why should they make any progress now? The skeptics believed that what little hope there was of proving the Taniyama-Shimura conjecture had now vanished. Their logic was that anything that might lead to a solution of Fermat's Last Theorem must, by definition, be impossible.

Even Ken Ribet, who had made the crucial breakthrough, was pessimistic: "I was one of the vast majority of people who believed that the Taniyama-Shimura conjecture was completely inaccessible. I didn't bother to try and prove it. I didn't even think about trying to prove it. Andrew Wiles was probably one of the few people on earth who had the audacity to dream that you can actually go and prove this conjecture."

In 1986 Andrew Wiles realized that it might be possible to prove Fermat's Last Theorem via the Taniyama-Shimura conjecture.

6

The Secret Calculation

. . . .

> An expert problem solver must be endowed with two in-
> compatible qualities — a restless imagination and a pa-
> tient pertinacity.
>
> Howard W. Eves

"It was one evening at the end of the summer of 1986 when I was sipping iced tea at the house of a friend," Wiles recalls. "Casually in the middle of a conversation he told me that Ken Ribet had proved the link between Taniyama-Shimura and Fermat's Last Theorem. I was electrified. I knew that moment that the course of my life was changing because this meant that to prove Fermat's Last Theorem all I had to do was to prove the Taniyama-Shimura conjecture. It meant that my childhood dream was now a respectable thing to work on. I just knew that I could never let that go. I just knew that I would go home and work on the Taniyama-Shimura conjecture."

Over two decades had passed since Andrew Wiles had discovered the library book that inspired him to take up Fermat's challenge, but now, for the first time, he could see a path toward achieving his childhood dream. Wiles says his attitude to Taniyama-Shimura changed overnight: "I remembered one mathematician who'd written about the Taniyama-Shimura conjecture and cheekily suggested it as an exercise for the interested reader. Well, I guess now I was interested!"

Since completing his Ph.D. with Professor John Coates at Cambridge, Wiles had moved across the Atlantic to Princeton University where he himself was now a professor. Thanks to Coates's guidance Wiles probably knew more about elliptic equations than anybody else in the world, but he was well aware that even with his enormous background knowledge and mathematical skills the task ahead was immense.

Most other mathematicians believed that embarking on the proof was a futile exercise. John Coates said: "I myself was very skeptical that the beautiful link between Fermat's Last Theorem and the Taniyama-Shimura conjecture would actually lead to anything, because I must confess I did not think that the Taniyama-Shimura conjecture was accessible to proof. Beautiful though this problem was, it seemed impossible to actually prove. I must confess I thought I probably wouldn't see it proved in my lifetime."

Wiles was aware that the odds were against him, but even if he ultimately failed to prove Fermat's Last Theorem he felt his efforts would not be wasted: "Of course the Taniyama-Shimura conjecture had been open for many years. No one had any idea how to approach it but at least it was mainstream mathematics. I could try and prove results, which, even if they didn't get the whole thing, would be worthwhile mathematics. I didn't feel I'd be wasting my time. So the romance of Fermat which had held me all my life was now combined with a problem that was professionally acceptable."

The Attic Recluse

At the turn of the century the great logician David Hilbert was asked why he never attempted a proof of Fermat's Last Theorem. He replied, "Before beginning I should have to put in three years of intensive study, and I haven't that much time to squander on a probable failure." Wiles knew that to have any hope of finding a proof he would first have to completely immerse himself in the problem, but unlike Hilbert he was prepared to take the risk. He read all the most recent journals and then played with the latest techniques over and over again until they became second nature to him. Gathering the necessary weapons for the battle ahead would require Wiles to spend the next eighteen months familiarizing himself with every bit of mathematics that had ever been applied to, or had been derived from, elliptic equations or modular forms. This was a comparatively minor investment, bearing in mind that he fully expected that any serious attempt on the proof could easily require ten years of single-minded effort.

Wiles abandoned any work that was not directly relevant to proving Fermat's Last Theorem and stopped attending the never-ending round of conferences and colloquia. Because he still had responsibilities in the Princeton mathematics department, Wiles continued to attend seminars, lecture to undergraduates, and give tutorials. Whenever possible he would avoid the distractions of being a faculty member by working at home, where he could retreat into his attic study. Here he would attempt to expand and extend the power of the established techniques, hoping to develop a strategy for his attack on the Taniyama-Shimura conjecture.

"I used to come up to my study, and start trying to find patterns. I tried doing calculations which explain some little piece of mathematics. I tried to fit it in with some previous broad conceptual understanding of some part of mathematics that would clarify the particular problem I was thinking about. Sometimes that would involve going and looking it up in a book to see how it's done there. Sometimes it was a question of modifying things a bit, doing a little extra calculation. And sometimes I realized that nothing that had ever been done before was any use at all. Then I just had to find something completely new — it's a mystery where that comes from.

"Basically it's just a matter of thinking. Often you write something down to clarify your thoughts, but not necessarily. In particular when you've reached a real impasse, when there's a real problem that you want to overcome, then the routine kind of mathematical thinking is of no use to you. Leading up to that kind of new idea there has to be a long period of tremendous focus on the problem without any distraction. You have to really think about nothing but that problem — just concentrate on it. Then you stop. Afterwards there seems to be a kind of period of relaxation during which the subconscious appears to take over, and it's during that time that some new insight comes."

From the moment he embarked on the proof, Wiles made the remarkable decision to work in complete isolation and secrecy. Modern mathematics has developed a culture of cooperation and collaboration, and so Wiles's decision appeared to hark back to a previous era. It was as if he was imitating the approach of Fermat himself, the most famous of mathematical hermits. Wiles explained that part of the reason for his decision to work in secrecy was his desire to work without being distracted: "I realized that anything to do with Fermat's Last Theorem generates too much interest. You can't really focus yourself for years unless you have undivided concentration, which too many spectators would have destroyed."

Another motivation for Wiles's secrecy must have been his craving for glory. He feared the situation arising whereby he had completed the bulk of the proof but was still missing the final element of the calculation. At this point, if news of his breakthroughs were to leak out, there would be nothing stopping a rival mathematician building on Wiles's work, completing the proof, and stealing the prize.

In the years to come Wiles was to make a series of extraordinary discoveries, none of which would be discussed or published until his proof was complete. Even close colleagues were oblivious to his research. John Coates can recall exchanges with Wiles during which he was given no clues as to what was going on: "I remember saying to him on a number of occasions, 'It's all very well this link to Fermat's Last Theorem, but it's still hopeless to try and prove Taniyama-Shimura.' I think he just smiled."

Ken Ribet, who completed the link between Fermat and Taniyama-Shimura, was also completely unaware of Wiles's clandestine activities. "This is probably the only case I know where someone worked for such a long time without divulging what he was doing, without talking about the progress he was making. It's just unprecedented in my experience. In our community people have always shared their ideas. Mathematicians come together at conferences, they visit each other to give seminars, they send E-mail to each other, they talk on the telephone, they ask for insights, they ask for feedback — mathematicians are always in communication. When you talk to other people you get a pat on the back; people tell you that what you've done is important, they give you ideas. It's sort of nourishing and if you cut yourself off from this, then you are doing something that's probably psychologically very odd."

In order not to arouse suspicion Wiles devised a cunning ploy that would throw his colleagues off the scent. During the early 1980s he had been working on a major piece of research on a particular type of elliptic equation, which he was about to publish in its entirety, until the discoveries of Ribet and Frey made him change his mind. Wiles decided to publish his research bit by bit, releasing another minor paper every six months or so. This apparent productivity would convince his colleagues that he was still continuing with his usual research. For as long as he could maintain this charade, Wiles could continue working on his true obsession without revealing any of his breakthroughs.

The only person who was aware of Wiles's secret was his wife, Nada. They married soon after Wiles began working on the proof, and as the calculation progressed he confided in her and her alone. In the years that followed, his family would be his only distraction. "My wife's only known me while I've been working on Fermat. I told her on our honeymoon, just a few days after we got married. My wife had heard of Fermat's Last Theorem, but at that time she had no idea of the romantic significance it had for mathematicians, that it had been such a thorn in our flesh for so many years."

Dueling with Infinity

In order to prove Fermat's Last Theorem Wiles had to prove the Taniyama-Shimura conjecture: Every single elliptic equation can be correlated with a modular form. Even before the link to the Last Theorem mathematicians had tried desperately to prove the conjecture, but every attempt had ended in failure. Wiles was well acquainted with the failures of the past: "Ultimately what one would naïvely have tried to do, and what people certainly did try to do, was to count elliptic equations and count modular forms, and show that there are the same number of each. But nobody has ever found any simple way of doing that. The first problem is that there are an infinite number of each and you can't count an infinite number. One simply doesn't have a way of doing it."

In order to find a solution, Wiles adopted his usual approach to solving difficult problems. "I sometimes write scribbles or doodles. They're not important doodles, just subconscious doodles. I never use a computer." In this case, as with many problems in number theory, computers would be of no use whatsoever. The Taniyama-Shimura conjecture applied to an infinite number of elliptic equations and, although a computer could check an individual case in a few seconds, it could never check all cases. Instead what was required was a logical step-by-step argument that would effectively give a reason and explain why every elliptic equation had to be modular. To find the proof Wiles relied solely on a piece of paper, a pencil, and his mind. "I carried this thought around in my head basically the whole time. I would wake up with it first thing in the morning, I would be thinking about it all day, and I would be thinking about it when I went to sleep. Without distraction I would have the same thing going round and round in my mind."

After a year of contemplation Wiles decided to adopt a general strategy known as *induction* as the basis for his proof. Induction is a powerful form of proof, because it can allow a mathematician to prove that a statement is true for an infinite number of cases by proving it for just one case. For example, imagine that a mathematician wants to prove that a statement is true for every counting number up to infinity. The first step is to prove that the statement is true for the number 1, which presumably is a fairly straightforward task. The next step is to show that if the statement is true for the number 1 then it must be true for the number 2, and if it is true for the number 2 then it must be true for the number 3, and if it is true for the number 3 then it must be true for the number 4, and so on. More generally, the mathematician has to show that if the statement is true for any number n, then it must be true for the next number $n + 1$.

Proof by induction is essentially a two-step process:

(1) Prove that the statement is true for the first case.
(2) Prove that if the statement is true for any one case, then it must be true for the next case.

Another way to think of proof by induction is to imagine the infinite number of cases as an infinite line of dominoes. In order to prove every case it is necessary to find a way of knocking down every one of the dominoes. Knocking them down one by one would take an infinite amount of time and effort, but proof by induction allows mathematicians to knock them all down by just knocking down the first one. If the dominoes are carefully arranged, then knocking down the first domino will knock down the second domino, which will in turn knock down the third domino, and so on to infinity. Proof by induction invokes the domino effect. This form of mathematical domino-toppling allows an infinite number of cases to be proved by just proving the first one. Appendix 10 shows how proof by induction can be used to prove a relatively simple mathematical statement about all numbers.

The challenge for Wiles was to construct an inductive argument that showed that each of the infinity of elliptic equations could be matched to each of the infinity of modular forms. Somehow he had to break the proof down into an infinite number of individual cases and then prove the first case. Next, he had to demonstrate that, having proved the first case, all the others would topple. Eventually he discovered the first step to his inductive proof hidden in the work of a tragic genius from nineteenth-century France.

Évariste Galois was born in Bourg-la-Reine, a small village just south of Paris, on October 25, 1811, just twenty-two years after the

Évariste Galois

French Revolution. Napoleon Bonaparte was at the height of his powers, but the following year saw the disastrous Russian campaign, and in 1814 he was driven into exile and replaced by King Louis XVIII. In 1815 Napoleon escaped from Elba, entered Paris, and reclaimed power, but within a hundred days he was defeated at Waterloo and forced to abdicate once again in favor of Louis XVIII. Galois, like Sophie Germain, grew up during a period of tremendous upheaval, but whereas Germain shut herself away from the turmoils of the French Revolution and concentrated on mathematics, Galois repeatedly found himself at the center of political controversy, which not only distracted him from a brilliant academic career, but also led to his untimely death.

In addition to the general unrest that impinged on everybody's life, Galois's interest in politics was inspired by his father, Nicolas-Gabriel Galois. When Évariste was just four years old his father was elected mayor of Bourg-la-Reine. This was during Napoleon's triumphant return to power, a period when his father's strong liberal values were in keeping with the mood of the nation. Nicolas-Gabriel Galois was a cultured and gracious man and during his early years as mayor he gained respect throughout the community, so even when Louis XVIII returned to the throne he retained his elected position. Outside of politics, his main interest seems to have been the composition of witty rhymes, which he would read at town meetings to the delight of his constituents. Many years later this charming talent for epigrams would lead to his downfall.

At the age of twelve Évariste Galois attended his first school, the Lycée of Louis-le-Grand, a prestigious but authoritarian institution. To begin with, he did not encounter any courses in mathematics and his academic record was respectable but not outstanding. However, one event occurred during his first term that would influence the course of his life. The Lycée had previously been a Jesuit school, and rumors began to circulate suggesting that it was about to be returned to the authority of the priests. During this period there was a continual struggle between republicans and monarchists to sway the balance of power between Louis XVIII and the people's representatives, and the increasing influence of the priests was seen as an indication of a shift away from the people and toward the King. The students of the Lycée, who in the main had republican sympathies, planned a rebellion, but the director of the school, Monsieur Berthod, uncovered the plot and immediately expelled the dozen or so ringleaders. The following day when Berthod demanded a demonstration of allegiance from the remaining senior scholars, they refused to drink a toast to Louis XVIII, whereupon another hundred students were expelled. Galois was too young to be involved in the failed rebellion and so remained at the Lycée. Nevertheless, watching his fellow students being humiliated in this way only served to inflame his republican tendencies.

It was not until the age of sixteen that Galois enrolled in his first mathematics class, a course that would, in the eyes of his teachers, transform him from a conscientious pupil into an unruly student. His school reports show that he neglected all his other subjects and concentrated solely on his newfound passion:

> This student works only in the highest realms of mathematics. The mathematical madness dominates this boy. I think it would be best for him if his parents would allow him to study nothing but this. Otherwise he is wasting his time here and does nothing but torment his teachers and overwhelm himself with punishments.

Galois's desire for mathematics soon outstripped the capacity of his teacher, and so he learned directly from the very latest books written by the masters of the age. He readily absorbed the most complex of concepts, and by the time he was seventeen he published his first paper in the *Annales de Gergonne*. The path ahead seemed clear for the prodigy, however, his own sheer brilliance was to provide the greatest obstacle to his progress. Although he obviously knew more than enough mathematics to pass the Lycée's examinations, Galois's solutions were often so innovative and sophisticated that his examiners failed to appreciate them. To make matters worse Galois would perform so many calculations in his head that he would not bother to outline clearly his argument on paper, leaving the inadequate examiners even more perplexed and frustrated.

The young genius did not help the situation by having a quick temper and a rashness that did not endear him to his tutors or anybody else who crossed his path. When Galois applied to the École Polytechnique, the most prestigious college in the land, his abruptness and lack of explanation in the oral examination meant that he was refused admission. Galois was desperate to attend the Polytechnique, not just because of its academic excellence but also because of its reputation for being a center for republican activism. One year later he reapplied and once again his logical leaps in the oral examination only served to confuse his examiner, Monsieur Dinet. Sensing that he was about to be failed for a second time and frustrated that his brilliance was not being recognized, Galois lost his temper and threw a blackboard eraser at Dinet, scoring a direct hit. Galois was never to return to the hallowed halls of the Polytechnique.

Undaunted by the rejections, Galois remained confident of his mathematical talent and continued his own private researches. His main interest concerned finding solutions to equations, such as quadratic equations. Quadratic equations have the form

$$ax^2 + bx + c = 0, \text{ where } a, b, c \text{ can have any value.}$$

The challenge is to find the values of x for which the quadratic equation holds true. Rather than relying on trial and error mathematicians would prefer to have a recipe for finding solutions, and fortunately such a recipe or formula exists:

$$x = \frac{-b \pm \sqrt{(b^2 - 4ac)}}{2a}.$$

Simply by substituting the values for a, b, and c into the above recipe one can calculate the correct values for x. For instance, we can apply the recipe to solve the following equation:

$$2x^2 - 6x + 4 = 0, \text{ where } a = 2, b = -6, \text{ and } c = 4.$$

By putting the values of a, b, and c into the recipe, the solution turns out to be $x = 1$ or $x = 2$.

The quadratic is a type of equation within a much larger class of equations known as polynomials. A more complicated type of polynomial is the cubic equation:

$$ax^3 + bx^2 + cx + d = 0.$$

The extra complication comes from the additional term x^3. By adding one more term x^4, we get the next level of polynomial equation, known as the quartic:

$$ax^4 + bx^3 + cx^2 + dx + e = 0.$$

By the nineteenth century, mathematicians also had recipes that could be used to find solutions to the cubic and the quartic equations, but there was no known method for finding solutions to the quintic equation:

$$ax^5 + bx^4 + cx^3 + dx^2 + ex + f = 0.$$

Galois became obsessed with finding a recipe for solving quintic equations, one of the great challenges of the era, and by the age of seventeen he had made sufficient progress to submit two research papers to the Academy of Sciences. The referee appointed to judge the papers was Augustin-Louis Cauchy, who many years later would argue with Lamé over an ultimately flawed proof of Fermat's Last Theorem. Cauchy was highly impressed by the young man's work and judged it worthy of being entered for the Academy's Grand Prize in Mathematics. In order to qualify for the competition the two papers would have to be resubmitted in the form of a single memoir, so Cauchy returned them to Galois and awaited his entry.

Having survived the criticisms of his teachers and rejection by the École Polytechnique Galois's genius was on the verge of being recognized, but over the course of the next three years a series of personal and professional tragedies would destroy his ambitions. In July of 1829 a new Jesuit priest arrived in the village of Bourg-le-Reine, where Galois's father was still mayor. The priest took exception to the mayor's republican sympathies and began a campaign to oust him from office by spreading rumors aimed at discrediting him. In particular the scheming priest exploited Nicolas-Gabriel Galois's reputation for composing clever rhymes. He wrote a series of vulgar verses ridiculing members of the community and signed them with the mayor's name. The elder Galois could not survive the shame and the embarrassment that resulted and committed suicide.

Évariste Galois returned to attend his father's funeral and saw for himself the divisions that the priest had created in the village. As the coffin was being lowered into the grave, a scuffle broke out between the Jesuit priest, who was conducting the service, and supporters of the mayor, who realized that there had been a plot to undermine him. The priest suffered a gash to the head, the scuffle turned into a riot, and the coffin was left to drop unceremoniously into its grave. Watching the French establishment humiliate and destroy his father served only to consolidate Galois's fervent support for the republican cause.

Upon returning to Paris, Galois combined his research papers into a single memoir. Well ahead of the competition deadline, he submitted it to the secretary of the Academy, Joseph Fourier, who in turn was supposed to pass it on to the judging committee. Galois's paper did not offer a solution to the quintic problem, but it did offer a brilliant insight and many mathematicians, including Cauchy, considered it to be a likely winner. To the shock of Galois and his friends, not only did he fail to win the prize, but he had not even been officially entered. Fourier had died a few weeks prior to the judging and, although a stack of competition entries was passed on to the committee, Galois's memoir was not among them. The memoir was never found, and the injustice was recorded by a French journalist.

> Last year before March 1st, Monsieur Galois gave to the secretary of the Institute a memoir on the solution of numerical equations. This memoir should have been entered in the competition for the Grand Prize in Mathematics. It deserved the prize, for it could resolve some difficulties that Lagrange had failed to do. Monsieur Cauchy had conferred the highest praise on the author about this subject. And what happened? The memoir is lost and the prize is given without the participation of the young savant.
>
> *Le Globe*, 1831

Galois felt that his memoir had been deliberately lost by a politically biased Academy, a belief that was reinforced a year later when the Academy rejected his next manuscript, claiming that "his argument is neither sufficiently clear nor sufficiently developed to allow us to judge its rigor." He decided that there was a conspiracy to exclude him from the mathematical community, and as a result he neglected his research in favor of fighting for the republican cause. By this time he was a student at the École Normale Supérieure, a slightly less prestigious college than the École Polytechnique. At the École Normale Galois's notoriety as a troublemaker was overtaking his reputation as a mathematician. This culminated during the July revolution of 1830 when Charles X fled France and the political factions fought for control in the streets of Paris. The École's director, Monsieur Guigniault, a monarchist, was aware that the majority of his students were radical republicans and so confined them to their dormitories and locked the gates of the college. Galois was being prevented from fighting alongside his brothers, and his frustration and anger were compounded when the republicans were eventually defeated. When the opportunity arose he published a scathing attack on the college director, accusing him of cowardice. Not surprisingly, Guigniault expelled the insubordinate student and Galois's formal mathematical career was at an end.

On December 4, the thwarted genius attempted to become a professional rebel by joining the Artillery of the National Guard, a republican branch of the militia otherwise known as the "Friends of the People." Before the end of the month the new king Louis-Phillipe, anxious to avoid a further rebellion, abolished the Artillery of the National Guard, and Galois was left destitute and homeless. The most brilliant young talent in all of Paris was being persecuted at every turn, and some of his former mathematical colleagues were becoming increasingly worried about his plight. Sophie Germain, who was by this time the shy elder stateswoman of French mathematics, expressed her concerns to friend of the family Count Libri-Carrucci:

> Decidedly there is a misfortune concerning all that touches upon mathematics. The death of Monsieur Fourier has been the final blow for this student Galois who, in spite of his impertinence, showed signs of a clever disposition. He has been expelled from the Ecole Normale, he is without money, his mother has very little also and he continues his habit of insult. They say he will go completely mad. I fear this is true.

As long as Galois's passion for politics continued it was inevitable that his fortunes would deteriorate further, a fact documented by the great French writer Alexandre Dumas. Dumas was at the restaurant Vendanges des Bourgogne when he happened upon a celebration banquet in honor of nineteen republicans acquitted of conspiracy charges:

> Suddenly, in the midst of a private conversation which I was carrying on with the person on my left, the name Louis-Phillipe, followed by five or six whistles, caught my ear. I turned around. One of the most animated scenes was taking place fifteen or twenty seats from me. It would be difficult to find in all Paris two hundred persons more hostile to the government than those to be found reunited at five o'clock in the afternoon in the long hall on the ground floor above the garden.
>
> A young man who had raised his glass and held an open dagger in the same hand was trying to make himself heard — Evariste Galois was one of the most ardent republicans. The

noise was such that the very reason for this noise had become incomprehensible. All that I could perceive was that there was a threat and that the name of Louis-Phillipe had been mentioned: the intention was made clear by the open knife.

This went way beyond my own republican opinions. I yielded to the pressure from my neighbor on the left who, as one of the King's comedians, didn't care to be compromised, and we jumped from the window sill into the garden. I went home somewhat worried. It was clear this episode would have its consequences. Indeed, two or three days later, Evariste Galois was arrested.

After being detained at Sainte-Pélagie prison for a month Galois was charged with threatening the King's life and brought to trial. Although there was little doubt from his actions that Galois was guilty, the raucous nature of the banquet meant that nobody could actually confirm that they had heard him make any direct threats. A sympathetic jury and the rebel's tender age — he was still only twenty — led to his acquittal. The following month he was arrested again.

On Bastille Day, July 14, 1831, Galois marched through Paris dressed in the uniform of the outlawed Artillery Guard. Although this was merely a gesture of defiance, he was sentenced to six months in prison and returned to Sainte-Pélagie. During the following months the teetotal youth was driven to drink by the rogues who surrounded him.

A week later a sniper in a garret opposite the prison fired a shot into a cell, wounding the man next to Galois. Galois was convinced that the bullet was intended for himself and that there was a government plot to assassinate him. The fear of political persecution terrorized him, and the isolation from his friends and family and rejection of his mathematical ideas plunged him into a state of depression. In a bout of drunken delirium he tried to stab himself to death, but his fellow republicans managed to restrain and disarm him.

In March 1832, a month before Galois's sentence was due to finish, a cholera epidemic broke out in Paris and the prisoners of Sainte-Pélagie were released. What happened to Galois over the next few weeks has been the subject of intense speculation, but what is certain is that the events of this period were largely the consequence of a romance with a mysterious woman by the name of Stéphanie-Félicie Poterine du Motel, the daughter of a respected Parisian physician. Although there are no clues as to how the affair started, the details of its tragic end are well documented.

Stéphanie was already engaged to a gentleman by the name of Pescheux d'Herbinville, who uncovered his fiancée's infidelity. D'Herbinville was furious and, being one of the finest shots in France, he had no hesitation in immediately challenging Galois to a duel at dawn. Galois was well aware of his challenger's reputation. During the evening prior to the confrontation, which he believed would be his last opportunity to commit his thoughts to paper, he wrote letters to his friends explaining his circumstances:

> I beg my patriots, my friends, not to reproach me for dying otherwise than for my country. I died the victim of an infamous coquette and her two dupes. It is in a miserable piece of slander that I end my life. Oh! Why die for something so little, so contemptible? I call on heaven to witness that only under compulsion and force have I yielded to a provocation which I have tried to avert by every means.

Despite his devotion to the republican cause and his romantic

Figure 19. The night before the duel Galois attempted to write down all his mathematical ideas. Other comments, however, also appear in the notes. On this page, on the left below center, are the words "Une femme" with the second word scribbled out, presumably a reference to the woman at the center of the duel.

involvement, Galois had always maintained his passion for mathematics and one of his greatest fears was that his research, which had already been rejected by the Academy, would be lost forever. In a desperate attempt to gain recognition he worked through the night writing out the theorems that he believed fully explained the riddle of quintic equations. Figure 19 shows one of the last pages written by Galois. The pages were largely a transcription of the ideas he had already submitted to Cauchy and Fourier, but hidden within the complex algebra were occasional references to "Stéphanie" or "une femme" and exclamations of despair — "I have not time, I have not time!" At the end of the night, when his calculations were complete, he wrote a covering letter to his friend Auguste Chevalier, requesting that, should he die, the papers be distributed to the greatest mathematicians in Europe:

My Dear Friend,

I have made some new discoveries in analysis. The first concern the theory of quintic equations, and others integral functions.

In the theory of equations I have researched the conditions for the solvability of equations by radicals; this has given me the occasion to deepen this theory and describe all the transformations possible on an equation even though it is not solvable by radicals. All this will be found here in three memoirs . . .

In my life I have often dared to advance propositions about which I was not sure. But all I have written down here has been clear in my head for over a year, and it would not be in my interest to leave myself open to the suspicion that I announce theorems of which I do not have a complete proof.

Make a public request of Jacobi or Gauss to give their opinions, not as to the truth, but as to the importance of these theorems. After that, I hope some men will find it profitable to sort out this mess.

I embrace you with effusion,

E. Galois

The following morning, Wednesday May 30, 1832, in an isolated field Galois and d'Herbinville faced each other at twenty-five paces armed with pistols. D'Herbinville was accompanied by seconds; Galois stood alone. He had told nobody of his plight: A messenger he had sent to his brother Alfred would not deliver the news of the duel until it was over and the letters he had written the previous night would not reach his friends for several days.

The pistols were raised and fired. D'Herbinville still stood, Galois was hit in the stomach. He lay helpless on the ground. There was no surgeon on hand and the victor calmly walked away, leaving his wounded opponent to die. Some hours later Alfred arrived on the scene and carried his brother to Cochin hospital. It was too late, peritonitis had set in, and the following day Galois died.

His funeral was almost as farcical as his father's. The police believed that it would be the focus of a political rally and arrested thirty comrades the previous night. Nonetheless two thousand republicans gathered for the service and inevitably scuffles broke out between Galois's colleagues and the government officials who had arrived to monitor events.

The mourners were angry because of a growing belief that d'Herbinville was not a cuckolded fiancé but rather a government agent, and that Stéphanie was not just a lover but a scheming seductress. Historians have argued about whether the duel was the result of a tragic love affair or politically motivated, but either way one of the world's greatest mathematicians was killed at the age of twenty, having studied mathematics for only five years.

Before distributing Galois's papers his brother and Auguste Chevalier rewrote them in order to clarify and expand the explanations. Galois's habit of explaining his ideas hastily and inadequately was no doubt exacerbated by the fact that he had only a single night to outline years of research. Although they dutifully sent copies of the manuscript to Carl Gauss, Carl Jacobi, and others, there was no acknowledgment of Galois's work for over a decade, until a copy reached Joseph Liouville in 1846. Liouville recognized the spark of genius in the calculation and spent months trying to interpret its meaning. Eventually he edited the papers and published them in his prestigious *Journal de Mathématique pures et appliquées*. The response from other mathematicians was immediate and impressive, because Galois had indeed formulated a complete understanding of how one could go about finding solutions to quintic equations. First Galois had classified all quintics into two types: those that were soluble and those that were not. Then, for those that were soluble, he devised a recipe for finding the solutions to the equations. Moreover, Galois examined equations of higher order than the quintic, those containing x^6, x^7, and so on, and could identify which of these were soluble. It was one of the masterpieces of nineteenth-century mathematics, created by one of its most tragic heroes.

In his introduction to the paper Liouville reflected on why the young mathematician had been rejected by his seniors and how his own efforts had resurrected Galois:

As Descartes said, "When transcendental questions are under discussion be transcendentally clear." Too often Galois neglected this precept; and we can understand how illustrious mathematicians may have judged it proper to try, by the harshness of their sage advice, to turn a beginner, full of genius but inexperienced, back on the right road. The author they censured was before them ardent, active; he could profit by their advice.

But now everything is changed. Galois is no more! Let us not indulge in useless criticisms; let us leave the defects there and look at the merits . . .

My zeal was well rewarded, and I experienced an intense pleasure at the moment when, having filled in some slight gaps, I saw the complete correctness of the method by which Galois proves, in particular, this beautiful theorem.

Toppling the First Domino

At the heart of Galois's calculations was a concept known as *group theory*, an idea that he had developed into a powerful tool capable of cracking previously insoluble problems. Mathematically, a group is a set of elements that can be combined together using some operation, such as addition or multiplication, and that satisfy certain conditions. An important defining property of a group is that, when any two of its elements are combined using the operation, the result is another element in the group. The group is said to be *closed* under that operation.

For example, the whole numbers form a group under the operation of "addition." Combining one whole number with another under the operation of addition leads to a third whole number, e.g.,

$$4 + 12 = 16.$$

All possible results under addition are within the whole numbers, and so mathematicians state that "the whole numbers are closed under addition" or "the whole numbers under addition form a group." On the other hand, the whole numbers do not form a group under the operation of "division," because dividing one whole number by another does not necessarily lead to another whole number, e.g.,

$$4 \div 12 = \tfrac{1}{3}.$$

The fraction $\tfrac{1}{3}$ is not a whole number and is outside the original group. However, by considering a larger group that does include fractions, the so-called rational numbers, closure can be reestablished: "the rational numbers are closed under division." Having said this, one stills needs to be careful because division by the element zero results in infinity, which leads to various mathematical nightmares. For this reason it is more accurate to state that "the rational numbers (excluding zero) are closed under division." In many ways closure is similar to the concept of completeness described in earlier chapters.

The whole numbers and the fractions form infinitely large groups, and one might assume that, the larger the group, the more interesting the mathematics it will generate. However, Galois had a "less is more" philosophy, and showed that small, carefully constructed groups could exhibit their own special richness. Instead of using the infinite groups, Galois began with a particular equation and constructed his group from the handful of solutions to that equation. It was groups formed from the solutions to quintic equations that allowed Galois to derive his results about these equations. A century and a half later, Wiles would use Galois's work as the foundation for his proof of the Taniyama-Shimura conjecture.

What makes the Taniyama-Shimura conjecture so hard to prove is that it is not merely an infinite problem, but rather it is an infinite number of infinite problems. First, in order to show that a particular elliptic equation is indeed paired with a modular form, every one of the infinite elements in the E-series (E_1, E_2, E_3, ...) has to be shown to be equal to every element in the corresponding M-series (M_1, M_2, M_3, ...). A mathematician could try to tackle this infinite problem by employing a proof by induction, that is to say, that each pairing of the infinite E- and M-series could be thought of as one domino in an infinite line of dominoes. The task is to topple the first domino (prove that $E_1 = M_1$), and then to show that if one domino falls, it will also topple the next one.

This task alone would be difficult enough, but to prove the Taniyama-Shimura conjecture it has to be repeated an infinite number of times, because there are an infinite number of elliptic and modular equations that all have to be paired off. This is equivalent to an infinite number of lines of dominoes, each line being infinite in length.

Faced with infinity piled upon infinity, Wiles realized that he could make an impact on the problem by exploiting the power of group theory. While Galois's original groups were built from the solutions of quintic equations, Wiles constructed his groups using a handful of solutions to each elliptic equation. After months of analysis Wiles used these elliptic groups to tentatively pair each elliptic equation with a candidate modular form. Furthermore, as part of this pairing process, Wiles could prove that the first element of each E-series did indeed match the first element of the associated M-series ($E_1 = M_1$).

Thanks to Galois, Wiles had effectively been able to set up the infinite number of infinitely long domino lines, and he had also toppled the first domino in every single row. Now the challenge was to show for every row of dominoes that if one domino fell, it would then topple the next. In other words, for all pairs of elliptic equations Wiles had to show that if one element of the *E*-series matched the corresponding element in the *M*-series, then so must the next elements match.

Getting this far had already taken two years, and there was no hint of how long it would take to find a way of extending the proof. Wiles relished the task ahead of him: "You might ask how could I devote an unlimited amount of time to a problem that might simply not be soluble. The answer is that I just loved working on this problem and I was obsessed. I enjoyed pitting my wits against it. Furthermore, I always knew that the mathematics I was thinking about, even if it wasn't strong enough to prove Taniyama-Shimura, and hence Fermat, would prove something. I wasn't going up a back alley; it was certainly good mathematics and that was true all along. There was certainly a possibility that I would never get to Fermat, but there was no question that I was simply wasting my time."

"Fermat's Last Theorem Solved?"

Although it was only the first step toward proving the Taniyama-Shimura conjecture, Wiles's Galois strategy was a brilliant mathematical breakthrough, worthy of publication in its own right. As a result of his self-imposed seclusion he could not announce the result to the rest of the world, but similarly he had no idea who else might be making equally significant breakthroughs.

Wiles recalls his philosophical attitude toward any potential rivals: "Well, obviously no one wants to spend years trying to solve something and then find that someone else just solves it a few weeks before you do. But curiously, because I was trying a problem that's considered impossible, I didn't really have much fear of competition. I simply didn't think I or anyone else had any real idea how to do it."

On March 8, 1988, Wiles was shocked to read front-page headlines announcing that Fermat's Last Theorem had been solved. The *Washington Post* and the *New York Times* claimed that thirty-eight-year-old Yoichi Miyaoka of the Tokyo Metropolitan University had discovered a solution to the world's hardest problem. At this stage Miyaoka had not yet published his proof, but only described its outline at a seminar at the Max Planck Institute for Mathematics in Bonn. British mathematician Don Zagier, who was in the audience, summarized the community's optimism, "Miyaoka's proof is very exciting, and some people feel that there is a very good chance that it is going to work. It's still not definite, but it looks fine so far."

In Bonn, Miyaoka had described how he had approached the problem from a completely new angle, namely differential geometry. For decades differential geometers had developed a rich understanding of mathematical shapes and in particular the properties of their surfaces. Then, in the 1970s, a team of Russians led by Professor S. Arakelov attempted to draw parallels between problems in differential geometry and problems in number theory. This was one strand of the Langlands program, and the hope was that unanswered problems in number theory could be solved by examining the corresponding question in differential geometry that had already been answered. This was known as the *philosophy of parallelism*.

Differential geometrists who tried to tackle problems in number theory became known as "arithmetic algebraic geometrists," and in 1983 they claimed their first significant victory, when Gerd Faltings at the Institute for Advanced Study at Princeton made a

Figure 20. These surfaces were created using the computer program *Mathematica*. They are geometrical representations of the equation $x^n + y^n = 1$, where $n = 3$ for the first image and $n = 5$ for the second. Here, x and y are regarded as complex variables.

major contribution toward understanding Fermat's Last Theorem. Remember that Fermat claimed that there were no whole number solutions to the equation:

$$x^n + y^n = z^n \text{ for } n \text{ greater than 2.}$$

Faltings believed he could make some progress toward proving the Last Theorem by studying the geometric shapes associated with different values of n. The shapes corresponding to each of the equations are all different, but they do have one thing in common — they are all punctured with holes. The shapes are four-dimensional, rather like modular forms, and a two-dimensional visualization of two of them is shown in Figure 20. All the shapes are like multidimensional doughnuts, with several holes rather than just one. The larger the value of n in the equation, the more holes there are in the corresponding shape.

Faltings was able to prove that, because these shapes always have more than one hole, the associated Fermat equation could only have a finite number of whole number solutions. A finite number of solutions could be anything from zero, which was Fermat's own claim, to a million or a billion. So Faltings had not proved Fermat's Last Theorem, but he had at least been able to discount the possibility of an infinity of solutions.

Five years later Miyaoka claimed he could go one step further. While still in his early twenties he had created a conjecture concerning the so-called Miyaoka inequality. It became clear that proof of his own geometrical conjecture would demonstrate that the number of solutions for Fermat's equation was not only finite, but zero. Miyaoka's approach was analogous to Wiles's in that they were both trying to prove the Last Theorem by connecting it to a fundamental conjecture in a different field of mathematics. In Miyaoka's case it was differential geometry; for Wiles the proof was via elliptic equations and modular forms. Unfortunately for Wiles he was still struggling to prove the Taniyama-Shimura conjecture when Miyaoka announced a full proof relating to his own conjecture, and therefore a proof of Fermat's Last Theorem.

Two weeks after his announcement in Bonn, Miyaoka released the five pages of algebra that detailed his proof, and then the scrutiny began. Number theorists and differential geometrists around the world examined the proof line by line, looking for the slightest gap in the logic or the merest hint of a false assumption. Within a few days several mathematicians highlighted what seemed to be a worrying contradiction within the proof. Part of Miyaoka's work led to a particular conclusion in number theory, which when translated back to differential geometry conflicted with a result that had already been proved years earlier. Although this did not necessarily invalidate Miyaoka's entire proof, it did clash with the philosophy of parallelism between number theory and differential geometry.

Another two weeks passed when Gerd Faltings, who had paved the way for Miyaoka, announced that he had pinpointed the exact reason for the apparent breakdown in parallelism — a gap in Miyaoka's logic. The Japanese mathematician was predominantly a geometrist, and he had not been absolutely rigorous in translating his ideas into the less familiar territory of number theory. An army of number theorists attempted to help Miyaoka patch up the error, but their efforts ended in failure. Two months after the initial announcement the consensus was that the original proof was destined to fail.

As with several other failed proofs in the past, Miyaoka had created new and interesting mathematics. Individual chunks of the proof stood on their own as ingenious applications of differential geometry to number theory, and in later years other mathematicians would build on them in order to prove other theorems, but never Fermat's Last Theorem.

The fuss over Fermat soon died down and the newspapers ran short updates explaining that the 300-year-old puzzle remained unsolved. No doubt inspired by all the media attention, a new piece of graffiti found its way onto New York's Eighth Street subway station:

$$x^n + y^n = z^n: \text{ no solutions}$$

I have discovered a truly remarkable proof of this,
but I can't write it now because my train is coming.

The Dark Mansion

Unknown to the world, Wiles breathed a sigh of relief. Fermat's Last Theorem remained unconquered and he could continue with his battle to prove it via the Taniyama-Shimura conjecture. "Much of the time I would sit writing at my desk, but sometimes I could reduce the problem to something very specific — there's a clue, something that strikes me as strange, something just below the paper which I can't quite put my finger on. If there was one particular thing buzzing in my mind then I didn't need anything to write with or any desk to work at, so instead I would go for a walk down by the lake. When I'm walking I find I can concentrate my mind on one very particular aspect of a problem, focusing on it completely. I'd always have a pencil and paper ready, so if I had an idea I could sit down at a bench and start scribbling away."

After three years of nonstop effort Wiles had made a series of breakthroughs. He had applied Galois groups to elliptic equations, he had broken the elliptic equations into an infinite number of pieces, and then he had proved that the first piece of every elliptic equation had to be modular. He had toppled the first domino and now he was exploring techniques that might lead to the collapse of all the others. In hindsight this seemed like the natural route to a proof, but getting this far had required enormous determination to overcome the periods of self-doubt. Wiles describes his experience of doing mathematics in terms of a journey through a dark unexplored mansion. "One enters the first room of the mansion and it's dark. Completely dark. One stumbles around bumping into the furniture, but gradually you learn where each piece of furniture is. Finally, after six months or so, you find the light switch, you turn it on, and suddenly it's all illuminated. You can see exactly where you were. Then you move into the next room and spend another six months in the dark. So each of these breakthroughs, while sometimes they're momentary, sometimes over a period of a day or two, they are the culmination of, and couldn't exist without, the many months of stumbling around in the dark that precede them."

In 1990 Wiles found himself in what seemed to be the darkest room of all. He had been exploring it for almost two years. He still had no way of showing that if one piece of the elliptic equation was modular then so was the next piece. Having tried every tool and technique in the published literature, he had found that they were all inadequate. "I really believed that I was on the right track, but that did not mean that I would necessarily reach my goal. It could be that the methods needed to solve this particular problem may simply be beyond present-day mathematics. Perhaps the methods I needed to complete the proof would not be invented for a hundred years. So even if I was on the right track, I could be living in the wrong century."

Wiles persevered for another year. He began working on a technique called Iwasawa theory. Iwasawa theory was a method of analyzing elliptic equations that he had learned as a student in Cambridge under John Coates. Although the method as it stood was inadequate, he hoped that he could modify it and make it powerful enough to generate a domino effect.

The Method of Kolyvagin and Flach

Since making the initial breakthrough with Galois groups, Wiles had become increasingly frustrated. Whenever the pressure became too great, he would turn to his family. Since be-

ginning work on Fermat's Last Theorem in 1986, he had become a father twice over. "The only way I could relax was
when I was with my children. Young children simply aren't interested in Fermat, they just want to hear a story and they're
not going to let you do anything else."

By the summer of 1991 Wiles felt he had lost the battle to
adapt Iwasawa theory. He had to prove that every domino, if it itself had been toppled, would topple the next domino — that if
one element in the elliptic equation E-series matched one element in the modular form M-series, then so would the next
one. He also had to be sure that this would be the case for every
elliptic equation and every modular form. Iwasawa theory could
not give him the guarantee he required. He completed another
exhaustive search of the literature and was still unable to find an
alternative technique that would give him the breakthrough he
needed. Having been a virtual recluse in Princeton for the last
five years, he decided it was time to get back into circulation in
order to find out the latest mathematical gossip. Perhaps somebody somewhere was working on an innovative new technique,
and as yet, for whatever reason, had not published it. He headed
north to Boston to attend a major conference on elliptic equations, where he would be sure of meeting the major players in
the subject.

Wiles was welcomed by colleagues from around the world,
who were delighted to see him after such a long absence from
the conference circuit. They were still unaware of what he had
been working on, and Wiles was careful not to give away any
clues. They did not suspect his ulterior motive when he asked
them the latest news concerning elliptic equations. Initially the
responses were of no relevance to Wiles's plight, but an encounter with his former supervisor John Coates was more fruitful:

"Coates mentioned to me that a student of his named Matheus Flach was writing a beautiful paper in which he was analyzing elliptic equations. He was building on a recent method devised by Kolyvagin and it looked as though his method was tailor-made for my problem. It seemed to be exactly what I needed, although I knew I would still have to further develop this so-called Kolyvagin-Flach method. I put aside completely the old approach I'd been trying and I devoted myself night and day to extending Kolyvagin-Flach."

In theory this new method could extend Wiles's argument from the first piece of the elliptic equation to all pieces of the elliptic equation, and potentially it could work for every elliptic equation. Professor Kolyvagin had devised a powerful mathematical method, and Matheus Flach had refined it to make it even more potent. Neither of them realized that Wiles intended to incorporate their work into the world's most important proof.

Wiles returned to Princeton, spent several months familiarizing himself with his newly discovered technique, and then began the mammoth task of adapting it and implementing it. Soon for a particular elliptic equation he could make the inductive proof work — he could topple all the dominoes. Unfortunately the Kolyvagin-Flach method that worked for one particular elliptic equation did not necessarily work for another elliptic equation. He eventually realized that all the elliptic equations could be classified into various families. Once modified to work on one elliptic equation, the Kolyvagin-Flach method would work for all the other elliptic equations in that family. The challenge was to adapt the Kolyvagin-Flach method to work for each family. Although some families were harder to conquer than others, Wiles was confident that he could work his way through them one by one.

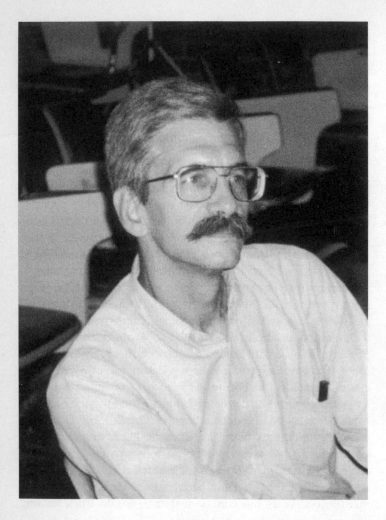

Nick Katz

After six years of intense effort Wiles believed that the end was in sight. Week after week he was making progress, proving that newer and bigger families of elliptic curves must be modular. It seemed to be just a question of time before he would mop up the outstanding elliptic equations. During this final stage of the proof, Wiles began to appreciate that his whole proof relied on exploiting a technique that he had discovered only a few months earlier. He began to question whether he was using the Kolyvagin-Flach method in a fully rigorous manner.

"During that year I worked extremely hard trying to make the Kolyvagin-Flach method work, but it involved a lot of sophisticated machinery that I wasn't really familiar with. There was a lot of hard algebra which required me to learn a lot of new mathematics. Then, in January of 1993, I decided that I needed to confide in someone who was an expert in the kind of geometric techniques I was invoking for this. I wanted to choose very carefully who I told, because they would have to keep it confidential. I chose to tell Nick Katz."

Professor Nick Katz also worked in Princeton University's mathematics department and had known Wiles for several years. Despite their closeness Katz was oblivious to what was going on literally just down the corridor. He recalls every detail of the moment Wiles revealed his secret: "One day Andrew came up to me at tea and asked me if I could come up to his office — there was something he wanted to talk to me about. I had no idea of what this could be. I went up to his office and he closed the door. He said he thought that he would be able to prove the Taniyama-Shimura conjecture. I was just amazed, flabbergasted — this was fantastic.

"He explained that there was a big part of the proof that relied on his extension of the work of Flach and Kolyvagin but it was pretty technical. He really felt shaky on this highly technical part of the proof and he wanted to go through it with somebody because he wanted to be sure it was correct. He thought I was the right person to help him check it, but I think there was another reason why he asked me in particular. He was sure that I would keep my mouth shut and not tell other people about the proof."

After six years in isolation Wiles had shared his secret. Now it was Katz's job to come to grips with a mountain of spectacular calculations based on the Kolyvagin-Flach method. Virtually everything Wiles had done was revolutionary, and Katz gave a great deal of thought as to the best way to examine it thoroughly: "What Andrew had to explain was so big and long that it wouldn't have worked to try and just explain it in his office in informal conversations. For something this big we really needed to have the formal structure of weekly scheduled lectures, otherwise the thing would just degenerate. That's why we decided to set up a lecture course."

They reckoned that the best strategy would be to announce a series of lectures open to the department's graduate students. Wiles would give the course and Katz would be in the audience. The course would effectively cover the part of the proof that needed checking, but the graduate students would have no idea of this. The beauty of disguising the checking of the proof in this way was that it would force Wiles to explain everything step by step, and yet it would not arouse any suspicion within the department. As far as everyone else was concerned this was just another graduate course.

"So Andrew announced this lecture course called 'Calculations on Elliptic Curves,'" recalls Katz with a sly smile, "which is a completely innocuous title — it could mean anything. He didn't mention Fermat, he didn't mention Taniyama-Shimura, he just started by diving right into doing technical calculations. There was no way in the world that anyone could have guessed what it was really about. It was done in such a way that unless you knew what this was for, then the calculations would just seem incredibly technical and tedious. And when you don't know what the mathematics is for, it's impossible to follow it. It's pretty hard to follow it even when you do know what it's for. Anyway, one by one the graduate students just drifted away and after a few weeks I was the only person left in the audience."

Katz sat in the lecture theater and listened carefully to every step of Wiles's calculation. By the end of it his assessment was that the Kolyvagin-Flach method seemed to be working perfectly. Nobody else in the department realized what had been going on. Nobody suspected that Wiles was on the verge of claiming the most important prize in mathematics. Their plan had been a success.

Once the lecture series was over Wiles devoted all his efforts to completing the proof. He had successfully applied the Kolyvagin-Flach method to family after family of elliptic equations, and by this stage only one family refused to submit to the technique. Wiles describes how he attempted to complete the last element of the proof: "One morning in late May, Nada was out with the children and I was sitting at my desk thinking about the remaining family of elliptic equations. I was casually looking at a paper of Barry Mazur's and there was one sentence there that just caught my attention. It mentioned a nineteenth-century construction, and I suddenly realized that I should be able to use that to make the Kolyvagin-Flach method work on the final family of elliptic equations. I went on into the afternoon and I forgot to go down for lunch, and by about three or four o'clock I was really convinced that this would solve the last remaining problem. It got to about teatime and I went downstairs and Nada was very surprised that I'd arrived so late. Then I told her — I'd solved Fermat's Last Theorem."

The Lecture of the Century

After seven years of single-minded effort Wiles had completed a proof of the Taniyama-Shimura conjecture. As a consequence, and after thirty years of dreaming about it, he had also proved Fermat's Last Theorem. It was now time to tell the rest of the world.

"So by May 1993, I was convinced that I had the whole of Fermat's Last Theorem in my hands," recalls Wiles. "I still wanted to check the proof some more, but there was a conference which was coming up at the end of June in Cambridge, and I thought that would be a wonderful place to announce the proof — it's my old hometown, and I'd been a graduate student there."

The conference was being held at the Isaac Newton Institute. The institute had planned a workshop on number theory with the obscure title "*L*-functions and Arithmetic." One of the organizers was Wiles's Ph.D. supervisor, John Coates: "We brought people from all around the world who were working on this general circle of problems and, of course, Andrew was one of the people that we invited. We'd planned one week of concentrated lectures and originally, because there was a lot of demand for lecture slots, I only gave Andrew two lecture slots. But then I gathered he needed a third slot, and so in fact I arranged to give up my own slot for his third lecture. I knew that he had some big result to announce, but I had no idea what."

When Wiles arrived in Cambridge he had two and a half weeks before his lectures began and wanted to make the most of the opportunity: "I decided I would check the proof with one or two experts, in particular the Kolyvagin-Flach part. The first person I gave it to was Barry Mazur. I think I said to him, 'I have a manuscript here with a proof to a certain theorem.' He looked very baffled for a while, and then I said, 'Well, have a look at it.' I think it then took him some time to register. He appeared stunned. Anyway I told him that I was hoping to speak about it at the conference, and that I'd really like him to try and check it."

One by one the most eminent figures in number theory began to arrive at the Newton Institute, including Ken Ribet, whose calculation in 1986 had inspired Wiles's seven-year ordeal. "I arrived at this conference on L-functions and elliptic curves and it didn't seem to be anything out of the ordinary until people started telling me that they had been hearing weird rumors about Andrew Wiles's proposed series of lectures. The rumor was that he had proved Fermat's Last Theorem, and I just thought this was completely nuts. I thought it couldn't possibly be true. There are lots of cases when rumors start circulating in mathematics, especially through electronic mail, and experience shows that you shouldn't put too much stock in them. But the rumors were very persistent, and Andrew was refusing to answer questions about it and he was behaving very, very queerly. John Coates said to him, 'Andrew, what have you proved? Shall we call the press?' Andrew just kind of shook his head and sort of kept his lips sealed. He was really going for high drama.

"Then one afternoon Andrew came up to me and started asking me about what I'd done in 1986 and some of the history of Frey's ideas. I thought to myself, this is incredible, he must have proved the Taniyama-Shimura conjecture and Fermat's Last Theorem, otherwise he wouldn't be asking me this. I didn't ask him directly if this was true, because I saw that he was behaving very coyly and I knew I wouldn't get a straight answer. So I just kind of said, 'Well, Andrew, if you have occasion to speak about this work, here's what happened.' I sort of looked at him as though I knew something, but I didn't really know what was going on. I was still just guessing."

Wiles's reaction to the rumors and the mounting pressure was simple: "People would ask me, leading up to my lectures, what exactly I was going to say. So I said, well, come to my lectures and see."

The title of Wiles's lecture series was "Modular Forms, Elliptic Curves, and Galois Representations." Once again, as with the graduate lectures he had given earlier in the year for the benefit of Nick Katz, the title of the lectures was so vague that it gave no hint of his ultimate aim. Wiles's first lecture was apparently mundane, laying the foundations for his attack on the Taniyama-Shimura conjecture in the second and third. The majority of his audience were completely unaware of the gossip, did not appreciate the point of the lectures, and paid little attention to the details. Those in the know were looking for the slightest clue that might give credence to the rumors.

Immediately after the lecture ended the rumor mill started again with renewed vigor, and electronic mail flew around the world. Professor Karl Rubin, a former student of Wiles, reported back to his colleagues in America:

Date: Mon, 21 Jun 1993 13:33:06
Subject: Wiles

Hi.   Andrew gave his first talk today. He did not announce a proof of Taniyama-Shimura, but he is moving in that direction and he has two more lectures. He is still being very secretive about the final result.

My best guess is that he is going to prove that if E is an elliptic curve over Q and the Galois representation on the points of order 3 on E satisfies certain hypotheses, then E is modular. From what he has said it seems he will not prove the full conjecture.

What I don't know is whether this will apply to Frey's curve, and therefore say something about Fermat. I'll keep you posted.

Karl Rubin
Ohio State University

That afternoon one of the graduate students who had attended Wiles's lecture dashed to the betting shop to bet £10 that Fermat's Last Theorem would be solved within the week. However, the bookmaker smelled a rat and refused to accept the wager. This was the third mathematician to have approached him that day, all of them asking to place the identical bet. Despite the fact that Fermat's Last Theorem had baffled the greatest minds on the planet for over three centuries, even bookmakers were beginning to suspect that it was on the verge of being proved.

By the following day more people had heard the gossip, and so the audience for the second lecture was significantly larger. Wiles teased them with an intermediate calculation which showed that he was clearly trying to tackle the Taniyama-Shimura conjecture, but the audience was still left wondering if he had done enough to prove it and, as a consequence, conquer Fermat's Last Theorem. A new batch of E-mails bounced off the satellites.

Date: Tue, 22 Jun 1993 13:10:39
Subject: Wiles

No more real news in today's lecture. Andrew stated a general theorem about lifting Galois representations along the lines I suggested yesterday. It does not seem to apply to all elliptic curves but the punchline will come tomorrow.

I don't really know why he is doing it this way. It's clear that he knows what he is going to say tomorrow. This is a truly massive piece of work that he has been working on for years, and he seems confident of it. I'll let you know what happens tomorrow.

Karl Rubin
Ohio State University

"On June 23, Andrew began his third and final lecture," recounts John Coates. "What was remarkable was that practically everyone who contributed to the ideas behind the proof was there in the room; Mazur, Ribet, Kolyvagin, and many, many others."

By this point the rumor was so persistent that everyone from the Cambridge mathematics community turned up for the final lecture. The lucky ones were crammed into the auditorium, while the others had to wait in the corridor, where they stood on tiptoe and peered through the window. Ken Ribet had made sure that he would not miss out on the most important mathematical announcement of the century: "I came relatively early and I sat in the front row along with Barry Mazur. I had my camera with me just to record the event. There was a very charged atmosphere and people were very excited. We certainly had the sense that we were participating in a historical moment. People had grins on their faces before and during the lecture. The tension had built up over the course of several days. Then there was this marvelous moment when we were coming close to a proof of Fermat's Last Theorem."

Barry Mazur had already been given a copy of the proof by Wiles, but even he was astonished by the performance. "I've never seen such a glorious lecture, full of such wonderful ideas, with such dramatic tension, and what a buildup. There was only one possible punch line."

After seven years of intense effort Wiles was about to announce his proof to the world. Curiously Wiles cannot remember the final moments of the lecture in great detail, but does recall the atmosphere: "Although the press had already got wind of what was happening, they were not at the lecture. But there were plenty of people in the audience who were taking photographs toward the end and the Director of the Institute certainly had come well prepared with a bottle of champagne. There was a typical dignified silence while I read out the proof and then I just wrote up the statement of Fermat's Last Theorem. I said, 'I think I'll stop here,' and then there was sustained applause."

The Aftermath

Strangely, Wiles was ambivalent about the lecture: "It was obviously a great occasion, but I had mixed feelings. This had been part of me for seven years: It had been my whole working life. I got so wrapped up in the problem that I really felt I had it all to myself, but now I was letting go. There was a feeling that I was giving up a part of me."

Wiles's colleague Ken Ribet had no such qualms: "It was a completely remarkable event. I mean, you go to a conference and there are some routine lectures, there are some good lectures, and there are some very special lectures, but it's only once in a lifetime that you get a lecture where someone claims to solve a problem that has endured for 350 years. People were looking at each other and saying, 'My God, you know we've just witnessed an historical event.' Then people asked a few questions about technicalities of the proof and possible applications to other equations, and then there was more silence and all of a sudden a second round of applause. The next talk was given by one Ken Ribet, yours truly. I gave the lecture, people took notes, people applauded, and no one present, including me, has any idea what I said in that lecture."

On June 23, 1993, Wiles gave a lecture at the Isaac Newton Institute in Cambridge. This was the moment immediately after he announced his proof of Fermat's Last Theorem. He, along with everyone else in the room, had no idea of the nightmare ahead.

While mathematicians were spreading the good news via E-mail, the rest of the world had to wait for the evening news or the following day's newspapers. TV crews and science reporters descended upon the Newton Institute, all demanding interviews with the "greatest mathematician of the century." The *Guardian* exclaimed, "The Number's Up for Maths' Last Riddle," and the front page of *Le Monde* read, "Le théorèm de Fermat enfin résolu." Journalists everywhere asked mathematicians for their expert opinion on Wiles's work, and professors, still recovering from the shock, were expected to briefly explain the most complicated mathematical proof ever, or provide a sound bite that would clarify the Taniyama-Shimura conjecture.

The first time Professor Shimura heard about the proof of his own conjecture was when he read the front page of the *New York Times* — "At Last, Shout of 'Eureka!' In Age-Old Math Mystery." Thirty-five years after his friend Yutaka Taniyama had committed suicide, the conjecture that they had created together had now been vindicated. For many professional mathematicians the proof of the Taniyama-Shimura conjecture was a far more important achievement than the solution of Fermat's Last Theorem, because it had immense consequences for many other mathematical theorems. The journalists covering the story tended to concentrate on Fermat and mentioned Taniyama-Shimura only in passing, if at all.

Shimura, a modest and gentle man, was not unduly bothered by the lack of attention given to his role in the proof of Fermat's Last Theorem, but he was concerned that he and Taniyama had been relegated from being nouns to adjectives. "It is very curious that people write about the Taniyama-Shimura conjecture, but nobody writes about Taniyama and Shimura."

This was the first time that mathematics had hit the headlines since Yoichi Miyaoka announced his so-called proof in 1988: The only difference this time was that there was twice as much coverage and nobody expressed any doubt over the calculation. Overnight Wiles became the most famous, in fact the only famous, mathematician in the world, and *People* magazine even listed him among "the 25 most intriguing people of the year," along with Princess Diana and Oprah Winfrey. The ultimate accolade came

Following Wiles's lecture, newspapers around the world reported his proof of Fermat's Last Theorem.

when an international clothing chain asked the mild-mannered genius to endorse their new line of menswear.

While the media circus continued and while mathematicians made the most of being in the spotlight, the serious work of checking the proof was under way. As with all scientific disciplines, each new piece of work had to be thoroughly examined before it could be accepted as accurate and correct. Wiles's proof had to be submitted to the ordeal of trial by referee. Although Wiles's lectures at the Isaac Newton Institute had provided the world with an outline of his calculation, this did not qualify as official peer review. Academic protocol demands that any mathematician submit a complete manuscript to a respected journal, the editor of which then sends it to a team of referees whose job it is to examine the proof line by line. Wiles had to spend the summer anxiously waiting for the referees' report, hoping that eventually he would get their blessing.

Andrew Wiles and Ken Ribet immediately following the historic lecture at the Isaac Newton Institute.

7

A Slight Problem

· · · · · · · · · · · · · · · · · ·

A problem worthy of attack
Proves its worth by fighting back.
                                    Piet Hein

As soon as the Cambridge lecture was over, the Wolfskehl committee was informed of Wiles's proof. The prize, bequeathed by the German industrialist in 1908, could not be awarded immediately because the rules of the contest demand verification by other mathematicians and publication of the proof:

> The *Königliche Gesellschaft der Wissenschaften* in Göttingen . . . will only take into consideration those mathematical memoirs which have appeared in the form of a monograph in the periodicals, or which are for sale in the bookshops . . . The award of the Prize by the Society will take place not earlier than two years after the publication of the memoir to be crowned. The interval of time is intended to allow German and foreign mathematicians to voice their opinion about the validity of the solution published.

Wiles submitted his manuscript to the journal *Inventiones Mathematicae*, whereupon its editor Barry Mazur began the process of selecting the referees. Wiles's paper involved such a variety of mathematical techniques, both ancient and modern, that Mazur made the exceptional decision to appoint not just two or three referees, as is usual, but six. Each year thirty thousand papers are published in journals around the world, but the sheer size and importance of Wiles's manuscript meant that it would undergo a unique level of scrutiny. To simplify matters the 200-page proof was divided into six sections and each of the referees took responsibility for one of these chapters.

Chapter 3 was the responsibility of Nick Katz, who had already examined that part of Wiles's proof earlier in the year: "I happened to be in Paris for the summer to work at the Institut des Hautes Etudes Scientifique, and I took with me the complete 200-page proof — my particular chapter was seventy pages long. When I got there I decided I wanted to have serious technical help, and so I insisted that Luc Illusie, who was also in Paris, become a joint referee on this chapter. We would meet a few times a week throughout that summer, basically lecturing to each other to try and understand this chapter. Literally we did nothing but look through this manuscript line by line to try and make sure that there were no mistakes. Sometimes we got confused by things and so every day, sometimes twice a day, I would E-mail Andrew with a question — I don't understand what you say on this page or it seems to be wrong on this line. Typically I would get a response that day or the next day which clarified the matter and then we'd go on to the next problem."

The proof was a gigantic argument, intricately constructed from hundreds of mathematical calculations glued together by thousands of logical links. If just one of the calculations was flawed or if one of the links became unstuck then the entire proof was potentially worthless. Wiles, who was now back in Princeton, anxiously waited for the referees to complete their task. "I don't like to celebrate full out until I have the paper completely off my hands. In the meantime I had my work cut out dealing with the questions I was getting via E-mail from the referees. I was still pretty confident that none of these questions would cause me much trouble." He had already checked and double-checked the proof before releasing it to the referees, so he was expecting little more than the mathematical equivalent of grammatical or typographic errors, trivial mistakes that he could fix immediately.

"These questions continued relatively uneventfully through till August," recalls Katz, "until I got to what seemed like just one more little problem. Sometime around August 23 I E-mail Andrew, but it's a little bit complicated so he sends me back a fax. But the fax doesn't seem to answer the question so I E-mail him again and I get another fax which I'm still not satisfied with."

Wiles had assumed that this error was as shallow as all the others, but Katz's persistence forced him to take it seriously: "I couldn't immediately resolve this one very innocent-looking question. For a little while it seemed to be of the same order as the other problems, but then sometime in September I began to realize that this wasn't just a minor difficulty but a fundamental flaw. It was an error in a crucial part of the argument involving the Kolyvagin-Flach method, but it was something so subtle that I'd missed it completely until that point. The error is so abstract that it can't really be described in simple terms. Even explaining it to a mathematician would require the mathematician to spend two or three months studying that part of the manuscript in great detail."

In essence the problem was that there was no guarantee that the Kolyvagin-Flach method worked as Wiles had intended. It was supposed to extend the proof from the first element of all elliptic equations and modular forms to cover all the elements, providing the toppling mechanism from one domino to the next. Originally the Kolyvagin-Flach method worked only under particularly constrained circumstances, but Wiles believed he had adapted and strengthened it sufficiently to work for all his needs. According to Katz this was not necessarily the case, and the effects were dramatic and devastating.

The error did not necessarily mean that Wiles's work was beyond salvation, but it did mean that he would have to strengthen his proof. The absolutism of mathematics demanded that Wiles demonstrate beyond all doubt that his method worked for every element of every *E*-series and *M*-series.

The Carpet Fitter

When Katz realized the significance of the error that he had spotted, he began to ask himself how he had missed it in the spring when Wiles had lectured to him with the sole purpose of identifying any mistakes. "I think the answer is that there's a real tension when you're listening to a lecture between understanding everything and letting the lecturer get on with it. If you interrupt every second — I don't understand this or I don't understand that — then the guy never gets to explain anything and you don't get anywhere. On the other hand, if you never interrupt you just sort of get lost and you're nodding your head politely, but you're not really checking anything. There's this real tension between asking too many questions and asking too few, and obviously by the end of those lectures, which is where this problem slipped through, I had erred on the side of too few questions."

Only a few weeks earlier, newspapers around the globe had dubbed Wiles the most brilliant mathematician in the world, and after 350 years of frustration number theorists believed that they had at last got the better of Pierre de Fermat. Now Wiles was faced with the humiliation of having to admit that he had made a mistake. Before confessing to the error he decided to try to make a concerted effort to fill in the gap. "I couldn't give up. I was obsessed by this problem and I still believed that the Kolyvagin-Flach method just needed a little tinkering. I just needed to modify it in some small way and then it would work just fine. I decided to go straight back into my old mode and completely shut myself off from the outside world. I had to focus again, but this time under much more difficult circumstances. For a long time I would think that the fix was just around the corner, that I was just missing something simple and it would all just fit into place the next day. Of course it could have happened that way, but as time went by it seemed that the problem just became more intransigent."

The hope was that he could fix the mistake before the mathematical community was aware that a mistake even existed. Wiles's wife, who had already witnessed the seven years of effort that had gone into the original proof, now had to watch her husband's agonizing struggle with an error that could destroy everything. Wiles remembers her optimism: "In September Nada said to me that the only thing she wanted for her birthday was a correct proof. Her birthday is on October 6. I had only two weeks to deliver the proof, and I failed."

For Nick Katz, too, this was a tense period: "By October the only people who knew about the error were myself, Illusie, the other referees of other chapters, and Andrew — in principle that was all. My attitude was that as a referee I was supposed to act in confidentiality. I certainly didn't feel that it was my business to discuss this matter with anyone except Andrew, so I just didn't say a word about it. I think externally he appeared normal but at this point he was keeping a secret from the world, and I think he must have been pretty uncomfortable about it. Andrew's attitude was that with just another day he would solve it, but as the fall went on, and no manuscript was available, rumors started circulating that there was a problem."

In particular, Ken Ribet, another of the referees, began to feel the pressure of keeping the secret: "For some completely accidental reason I became known as the 'Fermat Information Service.' There was an initial article in the *New York Times*, where Andrew asked me to speak to the reporter in his place, and the article said, 'Ribet, who is acting as a spokesperson for Andrew Wiles . . . ,' or something to that effect. After that I became a magnet for all kinds of interest in Fermat's Last Theorem, both from inside and outside the mathematics community. People were calling from the press, from all around the world in fact, and also I gave a very large number of lectures over a period of two or three months. In these lectures I stressed what a magnificent achievement this was and I outlined the proof and I talked about the parts that I knew best, but after a while people started getting impatient and began asking awkward questions.

"You see, Wiles had made this very public announcement, but no one outside of the very small group of referees had seen a copy of the manuscript. So mathematicians were waiting for this manuscript that Andrew had promised a few weeks after the initial announcement in June. People said, 'Okay, well this theorem has been announced — we'd like to see what's going on. What's he doing? Why don't we hear anything?' People were a little upset that they were being held in ignorance and they simply wanted to know what was going on. Then things got even worse because slowly this cloud gathered over the proof and people kept telling me about these rumors, which claimed there was a gap in chapter 3. They'd ask me what I knew about it, and I just didn't know what to say."

With Wiles and the referees denying any knowledge of a gap, or at the very least refusing to comment, speculation began to run wild. In desperation mathematicians began sending E-mails to each other in the hope of getting to the bottom of the mystery.

Subject: Gap in Wiles proof?
Date: 18 Nov 1993 21:04:49 GMT

There are many rumors buzzing around about one or more gaps in Wiles's proof. Does gap mean crack, fissure, crevasse, chasm, or abyss? Does anyone have reliable information?

Joseph Lipman
Purdue University

In every tearoom of every mathematics department the gossip surrounding Wiles's proof escalated every day. In response to the rumors and the speculative E-mails some mathematicians tried to return a sense of calm to the community.

Subject: Reply: Gap in Wiles proof?
Date: 19 Nov 1993 15:42:20 GMT

I don't have any firsthand information, and I don't feel at liberty to discuss secondhand information. I think the best advice for everyone is to keep calm and let the very competent referees who are carefully examining Wiles's paper do their work. They will report their findings when they have something definite to say. Anyone who has written a paper or refereed a paper will be familiar with the fact that often questions will arise in the process of checking proofs. It would be amazing were this not to happen for such an important result with a long difficult proof.

Leonard Evens
Northwestern University

Despite the calls for calm, the E-mails continued unabated. As well as discussing the putative error, mathematicians were now arguing over the ethics of preempting the referees' announcement.

Subject: More Fermat Gossip
Date: 24 Nov 93 12:00:34 GMT

I guess it's clear that I disagree with those who say we should not gossip about whether Wiles's proof of Fermat's Last Theorem is flawed or not. I am all in favor of this kind of gossip as long as it is not taken too seriously. I don't regard it as malicious. In particular because, whether or not Wiles's proof is flawed, I feel sure that he has done some world-class mathematics.

So, here is what I got today, nth-hand...

Bob Silverman

Subject: Re: Fermat hole
Date: Mon, 22 Nov 93 20:16 GMT

Coates said in a lecture at the Newton Institute here last week that in his opinion there is a gap in the "geometric Euler systems" part of the proof which "might take a week, or might take two years" to fill. I have spoken to him several times, but am still not sure on what basis he makes the claim: he does not have a copy of the manuscript.

As far as I know the only copy in Cambridge is with Richard Taylor as one of the referees of the paper for Inventiones, and he has consistently declined to comment until all the referees reach a common conclusion. So the situation is confused. Myself I don't see how Coates's view can be taken as authoritative at this stage: I plan to wait for word from Richard Taylor.

Richard Pinch

While the furor over his elusive proof was increasing, Wiles did his best to ignore the controversy and speculation. "I really shut myself off because I didn't want to know what people were saying about me. I just went into seclusion, but periodically my colleague Peter Sarnak would say to me, 'You know that there's a storm out there.' I'd listen, but, for myself, I really just wanted to cut myself off completely, just to focus completely on the problem."

Peter Sarnak had joined the Princeton Mathematics Department at the same time as Wiles, and over the years they had become close friends. During this intense period of turmoil Sarnak was one of the few people in whom Wiles would confide. "Well, I never knew the exact details, but it was clear that he was trying to overcome this one serious issue. But every time he would fix this one part of the calculation, it would cause some other difficulty in another part of the proof. It was like he was trying to put a carpet in a room where the carpet might be bigger than the room. So Andrew could fit the carpet in any one corner, only to find that it would pop up in another corner. Whether you could or could not fit the carpet in the room was not something he was able to decide. Mind you, even with the error, Andrew had made a giant step. Before him there was no one who had any approach to the Taniyama-Shimura conjecture, but now everybody got really excited because he showed us so many new ideas. They were fundamental, new things that nobody had considered before. So even if it couldn't be fixed this was a very major advance — but of course Fermat would still be unsolved."

Eventually Wiles realized that he could not maintain his silence forever. The solution to the mistake was not just around the corner, and it was time to put an end to the speculation. After an autumn of dismal failure he sent the following E-mail to the mathematical bulletin board:

Subject: Fermat Status
Date: 4 Dec 93 01:36:50 GMT

In view of the speculation on the status of my work on the Taniyama-Shimura conjecture and Fermat's Last Theorem I will give a brief account of the situation. During the review process a number of problems emerged, most of which have been resolved, but one in particular I have not settled. The key reduction of (most cases of) the Taniyama-Shimura conjecture to the calculation of the Selmer group is correct. However the final calculation of a precise upper bound for the Selmer group in the semistable case (of the symmetric square representation associated to a modular form) is not yet complete as it stands. I believe that I will be able to finish this in the near future using the ideas explained in my Cambridge lectures.

The fact that a lot of work remains to be done on the manuscript makes it still unsuitable for release as a preprint. In my course in Princeton beginning in February I will give a full account of this work.

Andrew Wiles

Few were convinced by Wiles's optimism. Almost six months had passed without the error being corrected, and there was no reason to think anything would change in the next six months. In any case, if he really could "finish this in the near future," then why bother issuing the E-mail? Why not just maintain the silence for a few more weeks and then release the finished manuscript? The

February lecture course that he mentioned in his E-mail failed to give any of the promised detail, and the mathematical community suspected that Wiles was just trying to buy himself extra time.

The newspapers leapt on the story once again and mathematicians were reminded of Miyaoka's failed proof in 1988. History was repeating itself. Number theorists were now waiting for the next E-mail that would explain why the proof was irretrievably flawed. A handful of mathematicians had expressed doubts over the proof back in the summer, and now their pessimism seemed to have been justified. One story claims that Professor Alan Baker at the University of Cambridge offered to bet one hundred bottles of wine against a single bottle that the proof would be shown to be invalid within a year. Baker denies the anecdote, but proudly admits to having expressed a "healthy skepticism."

Less than six months after his lecture at the Newton Institute, Wiles's proof was in tatters. The pleasure, passion, and hope that carried him through the years of secret calculations were replaced with embarrassment and despair. He recalls how his childhood dream had become a nightmare: "The first seven years that I worked on this problem I enjoyed the private combat. No matter how hard it had been, no matter how insurmountable things seemed, I was engaged in my favorite problem. It was my childhood passion, I just couldn't put it down, I didn't want to leave it for a moment. Then I'd spoken about it publicly, and in speaking about it there was actually a certain sense of loss. It was a very mixed emotion. It was wonderful to see other people reacting to the proof, to see how the arguments could completely change the whole direction of mathematics, but at the same time I'd lost that personal quest. It was now open to the world, and I no longer had this private dream which I was fulfilling. And then, after there was a problem with it, there were dozens, hundreds, thousands of people who wanted to distract me. Doing maths in that kind of rather overexposed way is certainly not my style, and I didn't at all enjoy this very public way of doing it."

Number theorists around the world empathized with Wiles's position. Ken Ribet had himself been through the same nightmare eight years earlier when he tried to prove the link between the Taniyama-Shimura conjecture and Fermat's Last Theorem. "I was giving a lecture about the proof at the Mathematical Sciences Research Institute in Berkeley and someone from the audience said, 'Well, wait a minute, how do you know that such and such is true?' I responded immediately, giving my reason, and they said, 'Well that doesn't apply in this situation.' I had an immediate terror. I kind of broke out into a sweat and I was very upset about it. Then I realized that there was only one possibility for justifying this, which was to go back to the fundamental work on the subject and see exactly how it was done in a similar situation. I looked in the relevant paper and I saw that the method did indeed apply in my case, and within a day or two I had the thing all fixed up. In my next lecture I was able to give the justification. But you always live with this fear that if you announce something important, a fundamental mistake can be discovered.

"When you find an error in a manuscript it can go two ways. Sometimes there's an immediate confidence and the proof can be resurrected with little difficulty. And sometimes there's the opposite. It's very disquieting, there's a sinking feeling when you realize that you've made a fundamental error and there's no way to repair it. It's possible that when a hole develops the theorem really just falls apart completely, because the more you try to patch it the more trouble you get into. But in Wiles's case each chapter of the proof was a significant article in its own right. The manuscript was seven years' work, it was basically several important papers pieced together and each one of the papers has a great deal of interest. The error occurred in one of the papers, in chapter 3, but even if you take out chapter 3 what remained was absolutely wonderful."

But without chapter 3 there was no proof of the Taniyama-Shimura conjecture and therefore no proof of Fermat's Last Theorem. There was a sense of frustration in the mathematical community that the proof behind two great problems was in jeopardy. Moreover, after six months of waiting still nobody, beyond Wiles and the referees, had access to the manuscript. There was a growing clamor for more openness, so everyone could see for themselves the details of the error. The hope was that somebody somewhere might see something that Wiles had missed, and conjure up a calculation to fix the gap in the proof. Some mathematicians claimed that the proof was too valuable to be left in the hands of just one man. Number theorists had become the butt of gibes from other mathematicians, who sarcastically questioned whether or not they understood the concept of proof. What should have been the proudest moment in the history of mathematics was turning into a joke.

Despite the pressure Wiles refused to release the manuscript. After seven years of devoted effort he was not ready to sit back and watch someone else complete the proof and steal the glory. The person who proves Fermat's Last Theorem is not the person who puts in the most work, it's the person who delivers the final and complete proof. Wiles knew that once the manuscript was published in its flawed state he would immediately be swamped by questions and demands for clarification from would-be gap-fixers, and these distractions would destroy his own hopes of mending the proof while giving others vital clues.

Wiles attempted to return to the same state of isolation that had allowed him to create the original proof, and reverted to his habit of studying intensely in his attic. Occasionally he would wander down by the Princeton lake, as he had done in the past. The joggers, cyclists, and rowers who had previously passed him by with a brief wave now stopped and asked him whether there was any progress with the gap. Wiles had appeared on front pages around the world, he had been featured in *People* magazine, and he had even been interviewed on CNN. The previous summer Wiles had become the world's first mathematical celebrity, and already his image was tarnished.

Meanwhile, back in the mathematics department the gossip continued. Princeton mathematician Professor John H. Conway remembers the atmosphere in the department's tearoom: "We'd gather for tea at 3 o'clock and make a rush for the cookies. Sometimes we'd discuss mathematical problems, sometimes we'd discuss the O. J. Simpson trial, and sometimes we'd discuss Andrew's progress. Because nobody actually liked to come out and ask him how he's getting on with the proof, we were behaving a little bit like Kremlinologists. So somebody would say: 'I saw Andrew this morning' — 'Did he smile?' — 'Well, yes, but he didn't look too happy.' We could only gauge his feelings by his face."

The Nightmare E-mail

As winter deepened, hopes of a breakthrough faded, and more mathematicians argued that it was Wiles's duty to release the manuscript. The rumors continued and one newspaper article claimed that Wiles had given up and that the proof had irrevocably collapsed. Although this was an exaggeration, it was certainly true that Wiles had exhausted dozens of approaches that might have circumvented the error and he could see no other potential routes to a solution.

Wiles admitted to Peter Sarnak that the situation was getting desperate and that he was on the point of accepting defeat. Sarnak suggested that part of the difficulty was that Wiles had nobody he could trust on a day-to-day basis; there was nobody he could bounce ideas off or who could inspire him to explore more lateral approaches. He suggested that Wiles take somebody into his confidence and try once more to fill the gap. Wiles needed somebody who was an expert in manipulating the Kolyvagin-Flach method and who could also keep the details of the problem secret. After giving the matter prolonged thought, he decided to invite Richard Taylor, a Cambridge lecturer, to Princeton to work alongside him.

Taylor was one of the referees responsible for verifying the proof and a former student of Wiles, and as such he could be doubly trusted. The previous year he had been in the audience at the Isaac Newton Institute watching his former supervisor present the proof of the century. Now it was his job to help rescue the flawed proof.

By January Wiles, with the help of Taylor, was once again tirelessly exploring the Kolyvagin-Flach method, trying to find a way out of the problem. Occasionally after days of effort they would enter new territory, but inevitably they would find themselves back where they started. Having ventured farther than ever before and failing over and over again, they both realized that they were in the heart of an unimaginably vast labyrinth. Their deepest fear was that the labyrinth was infinite and without exit, and that they would be doomed to wander aimlessly and endlessly.

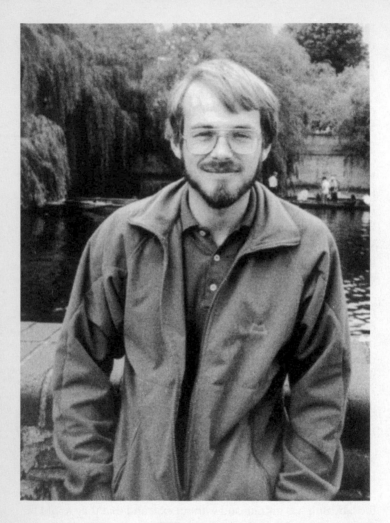

Richard Taylor

Then, in the spring of 1994, just when it looked as though things could not get any worse, the following E-mail hit computer screens around the world:

Date :   03 April 94
SUBJECT: Fermat again!

There has been a really amazing development today on Fermat's Last Theorem.

Noam Elkies has announced a counterexample, so that Fermat's Last Theorem is not true after all! He spoke about this at the Institute today. The solution to Fermat that he constructs involves an incredibly large prime exponent (larger than 10^{20}), but it is constructive. The main idea seems to be a kind of Heegner point construction, combined with a really ingenious descent for passing from the modular curves to the Fermat curve. The really difficult part of the argument seems to be to show that the field of definition of the solution (which, a priori, is some ring class field of an imaginary quadratic field) actually descends to Q.

I wasn't able to get all the details, which were quite intricate . . .

So it seems that the Taniyama-Shimura conjecture is not true after all. The experts think that it can still be salvaged, by extending the concept of automorphic representation, and introducing a notion of "anomalous curves" that would still give rise to a "quasi-automorphic representation."

Henri Darmon
Princeton University

Noam Elkies was the Harvard professor who back in 1988 had

found a counterexample to Euler's conjecture, thereby proving that it was false:

$$2{,}682{,}440^4 + 15{,}365{,}639^4 + 18{,}796{,}760^4 = 20{,}615{,}673^4.$$

Now he had apparently discovered a counterexample to Fermat's Last Theorem, proving that it too was false. This was a tragic blow for Wiles — the reason he could not fix the proof was that the so-called error was a direct result of the falsity of the Last Theorem. It was an even greater blow for the mathematical community at large, because if Fermat's Last Theorem was false, then Frey had already shown that this would lead to an elliptic equation that was not modular, a direct contradiction to the Taniyama-Shimura conjecture. Elkies had not only found a counterexample to Fermat, he had indirectly found a counterexample to Taniyama-Shimura.

The death of the Taniyama-Shimura conjecture would have devastating repercussions throughout number theory, because for two decades mathematicians had tacitly assumed its truth. In Chapter 5 it was explained that mathematicians had written dozens of proofs that began with "Assuming the Taniyama-Shimura conjecture," but now Elkies had shown that this assumption was wrong and all those proofs had simultaneously collapsed. Mathematicians immediately began to demand more information and bombarded Elkies with questions, but there was no response and no explanation as to why he was remaining tight-lipped. Nobody could even find the exact details of the counterexample.

After one or two days of turmoil some mathematicians took a second look at the E-mail and began to realize that, although it was typically dated April 2 or April 3, this was a result of having received it second- or thirdhand. The original message was dated

April 1. The E-mail was a mischievous hoax perpetrated by the Canadian number theorist Henri Darmon. The rogue E-mail served as a suitable lesson for the Fermat rumormongers, and for a while the Last Theorem, Wiles, Taylor, and the damaged proof were left in peace.

That summer Wiles and Taylor made no progress. After eight years of unbroken effort and a lifetime's obsession, Wiles was prepared to admit defeat. He told Taylor that he could see no point in continuing with their attempts to fix the proof. Taylor had already planned to spend September in Princeton before returning to Cambridge, and so despite Wiles's despondency, he suggested they persevere for one more month. If there was no sign of a fix by the end of September, then they would give up, publicly acknowledge their failure, and publish the flawed proof to allow others an opportunity to examine it.

The Birthday Present

Although Wiles's battle with the world's hardest mathematical problem seemed doomed to end in failure, he could look back at the last seven years and be reassured by the knowledge that the bulk of his work was still valid. To begin with, Wiles's use of Galois groups had given everybody a new insight into the problem. He had shown that the first element of every elliptic equation could be paired with the first element of a modular form. Then the challenge was to show that if one element of the elliptic equation was modular, then so must the next be modular, and so must they all be modular.

During the middle years Wiles wrestled with the concept of

extending the proof. He was trying to complete an inductive approach and had wrestled with Iwasawa theory in the hope that this would demonstrate that if one domino fell then they all would. Initially Iwasawa theory seemed powerful enough to cause the required domino effect, but in the end it could not quite live up to his expectation. He had devoted two years of effort to a mathematical dead end.

In the summer of 1991, after a year in the doldrums, Wiles encountered the method of Kolyvagin and Flach and he abandoned Iwasawa theory in favor of this new technique. The following year the proof was announced in Cambridge and he was proclaimed a hero. Within two months the Kolyvagin-Flach method was shown to be flawed, and ever since the situation had only worsened. Every attempt to fix Kolyvagin-Flach had failed.

All of Wiles's work apart from the final stage involving the Kolyvagin-Flach method was still worthwhile. The Taniyama-Shimura conjecture and Fermat's Last Theorem might not have been solved; nevertheless he had provided mathematicians with a whole series of new techniques and strategies that they could exploit to prove other theorems. There was no shame in Wiles's failure, and he was beginning to come to terms with the prospect of being beaten.

As a consolation he at least wanted to understand why he had failed. While Taylor reexplored and reexamined alternative methods, Wiles decided to spend September looking one last time at the structure of the Kolyvagin-Flach method to try to pinpoint exactly why it was not working. He vividly remembers those final fateful days: "I was sitting at my desk one Monday morning, September 19, examining the Kolyvagin-Flach method. It wasn't that I believed I could make it work, but I thought that at least I could explain why it didn't work. I thought I was clutching at straws, but I wanted to reassure myself. Suddenly, totally unexpectedly, I had this incredible revelation. I realized that, although the Kolyvagin-Flach method wasn't working completely, it was all I needed to make my original Iwasawa theory work. I realized that I had enough from the Kolyvagin-Flach method to make my original approach to the problem from three years' earlier work. So out of the ashes of Kolyvagin-Flach seemed to rise the true answer to the problem."

Iwasawa theory on its own had been inadequate. The Kolyvagin-Flach method on its own was also inadequate. Together they complemented each other perfectly. It was a moment of inspiration that Wiles will never forget. As he recounted these moments, the memory was so powerful that he was moved to tears: "It was so indescribably beautiful; it was so simple and so elegant. I couldn't understand how I'd missed it and I just stared at it in disbelief for twenty minutes. Then during the day I walked around the department, and I'd keep coming back to my desk looking to see if it was still there. It was still there. I couldn't contain myself, I was so excited. It was the most important moment of my working life. Nothing I ever do again will mean as much."

This was not only the fulfillment of a childhood dream and the culmination of eight years of concerted effort, but having been pushed to the brink of submission Wiles had fought back to prove his genius to the world. The last fourteen months had been the most painful, humiliating, and depressing period of his mathematical career. Now one brilliant insight had brought an end to his suffering.

"So the first night I went back home and slept on it. I checked through it again the next morning and by 11 o'clock I was satisfied, and I went down and told my wife, 'I've got it! I think I've found it.' And it was so unexpected that she thought I was talking about a children's toy or something, and she said, 'Got what?' I said, 'I've fixed my proof. I've got it.'"

The following month Wiles was able to make up for the promise he had failed to keep the previous year. "It was coming up to Nada's birthday again and I remembered that last time I could not give her the present she wanted. This time, half a minute late for our dinner on the night of her birthday, I was able to give her the complete manuscript. I think she liked that present better than any other I had ever given her."

Subject: Update on Fermat's Last Theorem
Date: 25 Oct 1994 11:04:11

As of this morning, two manuscripts have been released:

Modular elliptic curves and Fermat's Last Theorem,
                                    by Andrew Wiles.

Ring theoretic properties of certain Hecke algebras,
                         by Richard Taylor and Andrew Wiles.

The first one (long) announces a proof of, among other things, Fermat's Last Theorem, relying on the second one (short) for one crucial step.

As most of you know, the argument described by Wiles in his Cambridge lectures turned out to have a serious gap, namely the construction of an Euler system. After trying unsuccessfully to repair that construction, Wiles went back to a different approach, which he had tried earlier but abandoned in favor of the Euler system idea. He was able to complete his proof, under the hypothesis that certain Hecke algebras are local complete intersections. This and the rest of the ideas described in Wiles's Cambridge lectures are written up in the first manuscript. Jointly, Taylor and

Wiles establish the necessary property of the Hecke algebras in the second paper.

The overall outline of the argument is similar to the one Wiles described in Cambridge. The new approach turns out to be significantly simpler and shorter than the original one, because of the removal of the Euler system. (In fact, after seeing these manuscripts Faltings has apparently come up with a further significant simplification of that part of the argument.)

Versions of these manuscripts have been in the hands of a small number of people for (in some cases) a few weeks. While it is wise to be cautious for a little while longer, there is certainly reason for optimism.

Karl Rubin
Ohio State University

Andrew Wiles

Epilogue

Grand Unified Mathematics

. . . .

> A reckless young fellow from Burma,
> Found proofs of the theorem of Fermat,
> He lived then in terror,
> Of finding an error,
> Wiles's proof, he suspected, was firmer!
>
> Fernando Gouvea

This time there was no doubt about the proof. The two papers, consisting of 130 pages in total, were the most thoroughly scrutinized mathematical manuscripts in history and were eventually published in *Annals of Mathematics* (May 1995).

Once again Wiles found himself on the front page of the *New York Times*, but this time the headline "Mathematician Calls Classic Riddle Solved" was overshadowed by another science story — "Finding on Universe's Age Poses New Cosmic Puzzle." While journalists were slightly less enthusiastic about Fermat's Last Theorem this time around, the mathematicians had not lost sight of the true significance of the proof. "In mathematical terms the final proof is the equivalent of splitting the atom or finding the structure of DNA," announced John Coates. "A proof of Fermat is a great intellectual triumph and one shouldn't lose sight of the fact that it has revolutionized number theory in one fell swoop. For me the charm and beauty of

Andrew's work has been that it has been a tremendous step for number theory."

During Wiles's eight-year ordeal he had brought together virtually all the breakthroughs in twentieth-century number theory and incorporated them in one almighty proof. He had created completely new mathematical techniques and combined them with traditional ones in ways that had never been considered possible. In doing so he had opened up new lines of attack on a whole host of other problems. According to Ken Ribet the proof is a perfect synthesis of modern mathematics and an inspiration for the future: "I think that if you were lost on a desert island and you had only this manuscript then you would have a lot of food for thought. You would see all of the current ideas of number theory. You turn to a page and there's a brief appearance of some fundamental theorem by Deligne and then you turn to another page and in some incidental way there's a theorem by Hellegouarch — all of these things are just called into play and used for a moment before going on to the next idea."

While science journalists eulogized over Wiles's proof of Fermat's Last Theorem, few of them commented on the proof of the Taniyama-Shimura conjecture that was inextricably linked to it. Few of them bothered to mention the contribution of Yutaka Taniyama and Goro Shimura, the two Japanese mathematicians who back in the 1950s had sown the seeds for Wiles's work. Although Taniyama had committed suicide over thirty years earlier, his colleague Shimura was there to witness their conjecture proved. When asked for his reaction to the proof, Shimura gently smiled and in a restrained and dignified manner simply said, "I told you so."

Chapter 1

This chapter is devoted to the study of certain Galois representations. In the first section we introduce and study Mazur's deformation theory and discuss various refinements of it. These refinements will be needed later to make precise the correspondence between the universal deformation rings and the Hecke rings in Chapter 2. The main results needed are Proposition 1.2 which is used to interpret various generalized cotangent spaces as Selmer groups and (1.7) which later will be used to study them. At the end of the section we relate these Selmer groups to ones used in the Bloch-Kato conjecture, but this connection is not needed for the proofs of our main results.

In the second section we extract from the results of Poitou and Tate on Galois cohomology certain general relations between Selmer groups as Σ varies, as well as between Selmer groups and their duals. The most important observation of the third section is Lemma 1.10(i) which guarantees the existence of the special primes used in Chapter 3 and [TW].

1. Deformations of Galois representations

Let p be an odd prime. Let Σ be a finite set of primes including p and let $\mathbf{Q}_\Sigma$ be the maximal extension of $\mathbf{Q}$ unramified outside this set and ∞. Throughout we fix an embedding of $\overline{\mathbf{Q}}$, and so also of $\mathbf{Q}_\Sigma$, in $\mathbf{C}$. We will also fix a choice of decomposition group D_q for all primes q in $\mathbf{Z}$. Suppose that k is a finite field of characteristic p and that

$$(1.1) \qquad \rho_0 \colon \operatorname{Gal}(\mathbf{Q}_\Sigma/\mathbf{Q}) \to \operatorname{GL}_2(k)$$

is an irreducible representation. In contrast to the introduction we will assume in the rest of the paper that ρ_0 comes with its field of definition k. Suppose further that $\det \rho_0$ is odd. In particular this implies that the smallest field of definition for ρ_0 is given by the field k_0 generated by the traces but we will not assume that $k = k_0$. It also implies that ρ_0 is absolutely irreducible. We consider the deformations $[\rho]$ to $\operatorname{GL}_2(A)$ of ρ_0 in the sense of Mazur [Ma1]. Thus if $W(k)$ is the ring of Witt vectors of k, A is to be a complete Noetherian local $W(k)$-algebra with residue field k and maximal ideal m, and a deformation $[\rho]$ is just a strict equivalence class of homomorphisms $\rho \colon \operatorname{Gal}(\mathbf{Q}_\Sigma/\mathbf{Q}) \to \operatorname{GL}_2(A)$ such that $\rho \bmod m = \rho_0$, two such homomorphisms being called strictly equivalent if one can be brought to the other by conjugation by an element of $\ker : \operatorname{GL}_2(A) \to \operatorname{GL}_2(k)$. We often simply write ρ instead of $[\rho]$ for the equivalence class.

The first page of Wiles's published proof, which goes on for over a hundred pages.

Like many of his colleagues, Ken Ribet feels that proving the Taniyama-Shimura conjecture has transformed mathematics: "There's an important psychological repercussion which is that people now are able to forge ahead on other problems that they were too timid to work on before. The landscape is different, in that you know that all elliptic equations are modular and therefore when you prove a theorem for elliptic equations you're also attacking modular forms and vice versa. You have a different perspective of what's going on and you feel less intimidated by the idea of working with modular forms because basically you're now working with elliptic equations. And, of course, when you write an article about elliptic equations, instead of saying that we don't know anything so we're going to have to assume the Taniyama-Shimura conjecture and see what we can do with it, now we can just say that we know the Taniyama-Shimura conjecture is true, so therefore such and such must be true. It's a much more pleasant experience."

Via the Taniyama-Shimura conjecture Wiles had unified the elliptic and modular worlds, and in so doing provided mathematics with a shortcut to many other proofs — problems in one domain could be solved by analogy with problems in the parallel domain. Classic unsolved elliptic problems dating all the way back to the ancient Greeks could now be reexamined using all the available modular tools and techniques.

Even more important, Wiles had made the first step toward Robert Langlands's grander scheme of unification — the Langlands program. There is now a renewed effort to prove other unifying conjectures between other areas of mathematics. In March 1996 Wiles shared the $100,000 Wolf Prize (not to be confused with the Wolfskehl Prize) with Langlands. The Wolf Committee was recognizing that while Wiles's proof was an astounding accomplishment in its own right, it had also breathed life into Langlands's ambitious scheme. Here was a breakthrough that could lead mathematics into the next golden age of problem-solving.

Following a year of embarrassment and uncertainty the mathematical community could at last rejoice. Every symposium, colloquium, and conference had a session devoted to Wiles's proof, and in Boston mathematicians launched a limerick competition to commemorate the momentous event. It attracted this entry:

> "My butter, garçon, is writ large in!"
> A diner was heard to be chargin',
> "I had to write there,"
> Exclaimed waiter Pierre,
> "I couldn't find room in the margarine."
>
> E. Howe, H. Lenstra, D. Moulton

The Prize

Wiles's proof of Fermat's Last Theorem relies on verifying a conjecture born in the 1950s. The argument exploits a series of mathematical techniques developed in the last decade, some of which were invented by Wiles himself. The proof is a masterpiece of modern mathematics, which leads to the inevitable conclusion that Wiles's proof of the Last Theorem is not the same as Fermat's. Fermat wrote that his proof would not fit into the margin of his copy of Diophantus's *Arithmetica*, and Wiles's 100 pages of dense mathematics certainly fulfills this criterion, but surely the Frenchman did not invent modular forms, the Taniyama-Shimura conjecture, Galois groups, and the Kolyvagin-Flach method centuries before anyone else.

If Fermat did not have Wiles's proof, then what did he have? Mathematicians are divided into two camps. The hardheaded skeptics believe that Fermat's Last Theorem was the result of a rare moment of weakness by the seventeenth-century genius. They claim that, although Fermat wrote "I have discovered a truly marvelous proof," he had in fact found only a flawed proof. The exact nature of this flawed proof is open to debate, but it is quite possible that it may have been along the same lines as the work of Cauchy or Lamé.

Other mathematicians, the romantic optimists, believe that Fermat may have had a genuine proof. Whatever this proof might have been, it would have been based on seventeenth-century techniques, and would have involved an argument so cunning that it has eluded everybody from Euler to Wiles. Despite the publication of Wiles's solution to the problem, there are plenty of mathematicians who believe that they can still achieve fame and glory by discovering Fermat's original proof.

Although Wiles had to resort to twentieth-century methods to solve a seventeenth-century riddle, he has nonetheless met Fermat's challenge according to the rules of the Wolfskehl committee. On June 27, 1997, Andrew Wiles collected the Wolfskehl Prize, worth $50,000. Fermat's Last Theorem had been officially solved.

Wiles realizes that in order to give mathematics one of its greatest proofs, he has had to deprive it of its greatest riddle: "People have told me that I've taken away their problem, and asked if I could give them something else. There is a sense of melancholy. We've lost something that's been with us for so long, and something that drew a lot of us into mathematics. Perhaps that's always the way with math problems. We just have to find new ones to capture our attention."

But what next will capture Wiles's attention? Not surprisingly for a man who worked in complete secrecy for seven years, he is refusing to comment on his current research, but whatever he is working on, there is no doubt that it will never fully replace the infatuation he had with Fermat's Last Theorem. "There's no other problem that will mean the same to me. This was my childhood passion. There's nothing to replace that. I've solved it. I'll try other problems, I'm sure. Some of them will be very hard and I'll have a sense of achievement again, but there's no other problem in mathematics that could hold me the way Fermat did.

"I had this very rare privilege of being able to pursue in my adult life what had been my childhood dream. I know it's a rare privilege, but if you can tackle something in adult life that means that much to you, then it's more rewarding than anything imaginable. Having solved this problem there's certainly a sense of loss, but at the same time there is this tremendous sense of freedom. I was so obsessed by this problem that for eight years I was thinking about it all the time — when I woke up in the morning to when I went to sleep at night. That's a long time to think about one thing. That particular odyssey is now over. My mind is at rest."

Appendixes

. . . .

Appendix 1. The Proof of Pythagoras's Theorem

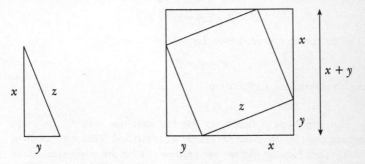

The aim of the proof is to show that Pythagoras's theorem is true for all right-angled triangles. The triangle shown above could be any right-angled triangle because its lengths are unspecified, and represented by the letters x, y, and z.

Also above, four identical right-angled triangles are combined with one tilted square to build a large square. It is the area of this large square that is the key to the proof.

The area of the large square can be calculated in two ways.

Method 1: Measure the area of the large square as a whole. The length of each side is $x + y$. Therefore, the area of the large square = $(x + y)^2$.

Method 2: Measure the area of each element of the large square. The area of each triangle is $\frac{1}{2}xy$, i.e., $\frac{1}{2} \times$ base $\times$ height. The area of the tilted square is z^2. Therefore,

$$\text{area of large square} = 4 \times (\text{area of each triangle}) + \text{area of tilted square}$$
$$= 4\left(\tfrac{1}{2}xy\right) + z^2.$$

Methods 1 and 2 give two different expressions. However, these two expressions must be equivalent because they represent the same area. Therefore,

$$\text{area from Method 1} = \text{area from Method 2}$$
$$(x + y)^2 = 4(\tfrac{1}{2}xy) + z^2.$$

The brackets can be expanded and simplified. Therefore,

$$x^2 + y^2 + 2xy = 2xy + z^2.$$

The $2xy$ can be canceled from both sides. So we have

$$x^2 + y^2 = z^2,$$

which is Pythagoras's theorem!

The argument is based on the fact that the area of the large square must be the same no matter what method is used to calculate it. We then logically derive two expressions for the same area, make them equivalent, and eventually the inevitable conclusion is that $x^2 + y^2 = z^2$, i.e., the square on the hypotenuse, z^2, is equal to the sum of the squares on the other two sides, $x^2 + y^2$.

This argument holds true for all right-angled triangles. The sides of the triangle in our argument are represented by x, y, and z, and can therefore represent the sides of any right-angled triangle.

Appendix 2. Euclid's Proof that $\sqrt{2}$ is Irrational

Euclid's aim was to prove that $\sqrt{2}$ could not be written as a fraction. Because he was using proof by contradiction, the first step was to assume that the opposite was true, that is to say, that $\sqrt{2}$ could be written as some unknown fraction. This hypothetical fraction is represented by p/q, where p and q are two whole numbers.

Before embarking on the proof itself, all that is required is a basic understanding of some properties of fractions and even numbers.

(1) If you take any number and multiply it by 2, then the new number must be even. This is virtually the definition of an even number.

(2) If you know that the square of a number is even, then the number itself must also be even.

(3) Finally, fractions can be simplified: $\frac{16}{24}$ is the same as $\frac{8}{12}$; just divide the top and bottom of $\frac{16}{24}$ by the common factor 2. Furthermore, $\frac{8}{12}$ is the same as $\frac{4}{6}$, and in turn $\frac{4}{6}$ is the same as $\frac{2}{3}$. However, $\frac{2}{3}$ cannot be simplified any further because 2 and 3 have no common factors. It is impossible to keep on simplifying a fraction forever.

Now, remember that Euclid believes that $\sqrt{2}$ cannot be written as a fraction. However, because he adopts the method of proof by contradiction, he works on the assumption that the fraction p/q does exist and then he explores the consequences of its existence:

$$\sqrt{2} = p/q.$$

If we square both sides, then

$$2 = p^2/q^2.$$

This equation can easily be rearranged to give

$$2q^2 = p^2.$$

Now from point (1) we know that p^2 must be even. Furthermore, from point (2) we know p itself must also be even. But if p is even, then it can be written as $2m$, where m is some other whole number. This follows from point (1). Plug this back into the equation and we get

$$2q^2 = (2m)^2 = 4m^2.$$

Divide both sides by 2, and we get

$$q^2 = 2m^2.$$

But by the same arguments we used before, we know that q^2 must be even, and so q itself must also be even. If this is the case, then q can be written as $2n$, where n is some other whole number. If we go back to the beginning, then

$$\sqrt{2} = p/q = 2m/2n.$$

The $2m/2n$ can be simplified by dividing top and bottom by 2, and we get

$$\sqrt{2} = m/n.$$

We now have a fraction m/n, which is simpler than p/q.

However, we now find ourselves in a position whereby we can repeat exactly the same process on m/n, and at the end of it we will generate an even simpler fraction, say g/h. This fraction can then be put through the mill again, and the new fraction, say e/f, will be simpler still. We can put this through the mill again, and repeat the process over and over again, with no end. But we know from point (3) that fractions cannot be simplified forever. There must always be a simplest fraction, but our original hypothetical fraction p/q does not seem to obey this rule. Therefore, we can justifiably say that we have reached a contradiction. If $\sqrt{2}$ could be written as a fraction, then the consequence would be absurd, and so it is true to say that $\sqrt{2}$ cannot be written as a fraction. Therefore $\sqrt{2}$ is an irrational number.

Appendix 3. The Riddle of Diophantus's Age

Let us call the length of Diophantus's life L. From the riddle we have a complete account of Diophantus's life, which is as follows:

> 1/6 of his life, $L/6$, was spent as a boy,
> $L/12$ was spent as a youth,
> $L/7$ was then spent prior to marriage,
> 5 years later a son was born,
> $L/2$ was the life span of the son,
> 4 years were spent in grief before he died.

The length of Diophantus's life is the sum of the above:

$$L = \frac{L}{6} + \frac{L}{12} + \frac{L}{7} + 5 + \frac{L}{2} + 4.$$

We can then simplify the equation as follows:

$$L = \frac{25}{28} L + 9,$$

$$\frac{3}{28} L = 9,$$

$$L = \frac{28}{3} \times 9 = 84.$$

Diophantus died at the age of 84 years.

Appendix 4. Bachet's Weighing Problem

In order to weigh any whole number of kilograms from 1 to 40 most people will suggest that six weights are required: 1, 2, 4, 8, 16, 32 kg. In this way, all the weights can easily be achieved by placing the following combinations in one pan:

$$1 \text{ kg} = 1,$$
$$2 \text{ kg} = 2,$$
$$3 \text{ kg} = 2 + 1,$$
$$4 \text{ kg} = 4,$$
$$5 \text{ kg} = 4 + 1,$$
$$\vdots$$
$$40 \text{ kg} = 32 + 8.$$

However, by placing weights in both pans, such that weights are also allowed to sit alongside the object being weighed, Bachet could complete the task with only four weights: 1, 3, 9, 27 kg. A weight placed in the same pan as the object being weighed effectively assumes a negative value. Thus, the weights can be achieved as follows:

$$1 \text{ kg} = 1,$$
$$2 \text{ kg} = 3 - 1,$$
$$3 \text{ kg} = 3,$$
$$4 \text{ kg} = 3 + 1,$$
$$5 \text{ kg} = 9 - 3 - 1,$$
$$\vdots$$
$$40 \text{ kg} = 27 + 9 + 3 + 1.$$

Appendix 5. Euclid's Proof That There Are an Infinite Number of Pythagorean Triples

A Pythagorean triple is a set of three whole numbers, such that one number squared added to another number squared equals the third number squared. Euclid could prove that there are an infinite number of such Pythagorean triples.

Euclid's proof begins with the observation that the difference between successive square numbers is always an odd number:

$$
\begin{array}{cccccccccc}
1^2 & 2^2 & 3^2 & 4^2 & 5^2 & 6^2 & 7^2 & 8^2 & 9^2 & 10^2 \ldots \\
1 & 4 & 9 & 16 & 25 & 36 & 49 & 64 & 81 & 100 \ldots \\
& 3 & 5 & 7 & 9 & 11 & 13 & 15 & 17 & 19 \quad \ldots
\end{array}
$$

In other words, every single one of the infinity of odd numbers can be added to a particular square number to make another square number. A fraction of these odd numbers are themselves square, but a fraction of infinity is also infinite.

Therefore there are also an infinity of odd square numbers that can be added to one square to make another square number. In other words there must be an infinite number of Pythagorean triples.

Appendix 6. Straying into Absurdity

The following is a classic demonstration of how easy it is to start off with a very simple statement and then within a few apparently straightforward and logical steps show that $2 = 1$.

First, let us begin with the innocuous statement

$$a = b.$$

Then multiply both sides by a, giving

$$a^2 = ab.$$

Then add $a^2 - 2ab$ to both sides:

$$a^2 + a^2 - 2ab = ab + a^2 - 2ab.$$

This can be simplified to

$$2(a^2 - ab) = a^2 - ab.$$

Finally, divide both sides by $a^2 - ab$, and we get

$$2 = 1.$$

The original statement appears to be, and is, completely harmless, but somewhere in the step-by-step manipulation of the equation there was a subtle but disastrous error that leads to the contradiction in the final statement.

In fact, the fatal mistake appears in the last step in which both sides are divided by $a^2 - ab$. We know from the original statement that $a = b$, and therefore dividing by $a^2 - ab$ is equivalent to dividing by zero.

Dividing anything by zero is a risky step, because zero will go into any finite quantity an infinite number of times. By creating infinity on both sides we have effectively torn apart both halves of the equation and allowed a contradiction to creep into the argument.

This subtle error is typical of the sort of blunder that caught out many of the entrants for the Wolfskehl Prize.

Appendix 7. Letter About Wolfskehl Prize

Dr. F. Schlichting was responsible for dealing with Wolfskehl entries during the 1970s. This letter, written to Paulo Ribenboim and published in his book *13 Lectures on Fermat's Last Theorem*, gives a unique insight into the work of the Wolfskehl committee:

Dear Sir,

There is no count of the total number of "solutions" submitted so far. In the first year (1907–1908) 621 solutions were registered in the files of the *Akademie*, and today they have stored about 3 metres of correspondence concerning the Fermat problem. In recent decades it was handled in the following way: the secretary of the *Akademie* divides the arriving manuscripts into:

(1) complete nonsense, which is sent back immediately,

(2) material which looks like mathematics.

The second part is given to the mathematical department, and there the work of reading, finding mistakes and answering is delegated to one of the scientific assistants (at German universities these are graduated individuals working for their Ph.D.) — at the moment I am the victim. There are about 3 or 4 letters to answer each month, and this includes a lot of funny and curious material, e.g. like the one sending the first half of his solution and promising the second if we would pay 1,000 DM in advance; or another one, who promised me 1% of his profits from publications, radio and TV interviews after he got famous, if only I would support him now; if not, he threatened to send it to a Russian mathematics department to deprive us of the glory of discovering him. From time to time someone appears in Göttingen and insists on personal discussion.

Nearly all "solutions" are written on a very elementary level (using the notions of high school mathematics and perhaps some undigested papers in number theory), but can nevertheless be very complicated to understand. Socially, the senders are often persons with a technical education but a failed career who try to find success with a proof of the Fermat problem. I gave some of the manuscripts to physicians who diagnosed heavy schizophrenia.

One condition of Wolfskehl's last will was that the *Akademie* had to publish the announcement of the prize yearly in the main mathematical periodicals. But already after the first years the periodicals refused to print the announcement, because they were overflowed by letters and crazy manuscripts.

I hope that this information is of interest to you.

Yours sincerely,
F. Schlichting

Appendix 8. The Axioms of Arithmetic

The following axioms are all that are required as the foundation for the elaborate structure of arithmetic:

1. For any numbers m, n

$$m + n = n + m \text{ and } mn = nm.$$

2. For any numbers m, n, k,

$$(m + n) + k = m + (n + k) \text{ and } (mn)k = m(nk).$$

3. For any numbers m, n, k

$$m(n + k) = mn + mk.$$

4. There is a number 0 which has the property that, for any number n,

$$n + 0 = n.$$

5. There is a number 1 which has the property that, for any number n,

$$n \times 1 = n.$$

6. For every number n, there is another number k such that

$$n + k = 0.$$

7. For any numbers m, n, k,

$$\text{if } k \neq 0 \text{ and } kn = km, \text{ then } m = n.$$

From these axioms other rules can be proved. For example, by rigorously applying the axioms and assuming nothing else, we can rigorously prove the apparently obvious rule that

$$\text{if } m + k = n + k, \text{ then } m = n$$

To begin with we state that

$$m + k = n + k.$$

Then by Axiom 6, let l be a number such that $k + l = 0$, so

$$(m + k) + l = (n + k) + l.$$

Then, by Axiom 2,

$$m + (k + l) = n + (k + l).$$

Bearing in mind that $k + l = 0$, we know that

$$m + 0 = n + 0.$$

By applying Axiom 4, we can at last declare what we set out to prove:

$$m = n.$$

Appendix 9. Game Theory and the Truel

Let us examine Mr. Black's options. First, Mr. Black could aim at Mr. Gray. If he is successful then the next shot will be taken by Mr. White. Mr. White has only one opponent left, Mr. Black, and as Mr. White is a perfect shot then Mr. Black is a dead man.

A better option is for Mr. Black to aim at Mr. White. If he is successful then the next shot will be taken by Mr. Gray. Mr. Gray hits his target only two times out of three and so there is a chance that Mr. Black will survive to fire back at Mr. Gray and possibly win the truel.

It appears that the second option is the strategy that Mr. Black should adopt. However, there is a third and even better option. Mr. Black could aim into the air. Mr. Gray has the next shot and he will aim at Mr. White, because he is the more dangerous opponent. If Mr. White survives then he will aim at Mr. Gray because he is the more dangerous opponent. By aiming into the air, Mr. Black is allowing Mr. Gray to eliminate Mr. White or vice versa.

This is Mr. Black's best strategy. Eventually Mr. Gray or Mr. White will die and then Mr. Black will aim at whoever survives. Mr. Black has manipulated the situation so that, instead of having the first shot in a truel, he has first shot in a duel.

Appendix 10. An Example of Proof by Induction

Mathematicians find it useful to have neat formulae that give the sum of various lists of numbers. In this case the challenge is to find a formula that gives the sum of the first n counting numbers.

For example, the sum of just the first number is 1, the sum of the first two numbers is 3 (i.e., $1 + 2$), the sum of the first three numbers is 6 (i.e., $1 + 2 + 3$), the sum of the first four numbers is 10 (i.e., $1 + 2 + 3 + 4$), and so on.

A candidate formula that seems to describe this pattern is:

$$\text{Sum}(n) = \tfrac{1}{2} n(n+1).$$

In other words, if we want to find the sum of the first n numbers, then we simply enter that number into the formula above and work out the answer.

Proof by induction can prove that this formula works for every number up to infinity.

The first step is to show that the formula works for the first case, $n = 1$. This is fairly straightforward, because we know that the sum of just the first number is 1, and if we enter $n = 1$ into the candidate formula we get the correct result:

$$\text{Sum}(n) = \tfrac{1}{2} n(n+1)$$
$$\text{Sum}(1) = \tfrac{1}{2} \times 1 \times (1+1)$$
$$\text{Sum}(1) = \tfrac{1}{2} \times 1 \times 2$$
$$\text{Sum}(1) = 1.$$

The first domino has been toppled.

The next step in proof by induction is to show that if the formula is true for any value n, then it must also be true for $n + 1$. If

$$\text{Sum}(n) = \tfrac{1}{2} n(n+1),$$

then,

$$\text{Sum}(n+1) = \text{Sum}(n) + (n+1)$$
$$\text{Sum}(n+1) = \tfrac{1}{2} n(n+1) + (n+1).$$

After rearranging and regrouping the terms on the right, we get

$$\text{Sum}(n+1) = \tfrac{1}{2}(n+1)\,[(n+1)+1].$$

What is important to note here is that the form of this new equation is exactly the same as the original equation except that every appearance of n has been replaced by $(n+1)$.

In other words, if the formula is true for n, then it must also be true for $n+1$. If one domino falls, it will always knock over the next one. The proof by induction is complete.

Suggestions for Further Reading

In researching this book I have relied on numerous books and articles. In addition to my main sources for each chapter, I have also listed other material that may be of interest to both the general reader and experts in the field. Where the title of the source does not indicate its relevance I have given a sentence or two describing its contents.

1. "I Think I'll Stop Here"

The Last Problem, by E.T. Bell, 1990, Mathematical Association of America. A popular account of the origins of Fermat's Last Theorem.

Pythagoras – A Short Account of His Life and Philosophy, by Leslie Ralph, 1961, Krikos.

Pythagoras – A Life, by Peter Gorman, 1979, Routledge and Kegan Paul.

A History of Greek Mathematics, Vols. 1 and 2, by Sir Thomas Heath, 1981, Dover.

Mathematical Magic Show, by Martin Gardner, 1977, Knopf. A collection of mathematical puzzles and riddles.

River meandering as a self-organization process, by Hans-Henrik Støllum, *Science* **271** (1996), 1710–1713.

2. The Riddler

The Mathematical Career of Pierre de Fermat, by Michael Mahoney, 1994, Princeton University Press. A detailed investigation into the life and work of Pierre de Fermat.

Archimedes' Revenge, by Paul Hoffman, 1988, Penguin. Fascinating tales that describe the joys and perils of mathematics.

3. A Mathematical Disgrace

Men of Mathematics, by E.T. Bell, Simon and Schuster, 1937. Biographies of history's greatest mathematicians, including Euler, Fermat, Gauss, Cauchy, and Kummer.

The periodical cicada problem, by Monte Lloyd and Henry S. Dybas, *Evolution* **20** (1966), 466–505.

Women in Mathematics, by Lynn M. Osen, 1994, MIT Press. A largely nonmathematical text containing the biographies of many of the foremost female mathematicians in history, including Sophie Germain.

Math Equals: Biographies of Women Mathematicians+Related Activities, by Teri Perl, 1978, Addison-Wesley.

Women in Science, by H. J. Mozans, 1913, D. Appleton and Co.

Sophie Germain, by Amy Dahan Dalmédico, *Scientific American,* December 1991. A short article describing the life and work of Sophie Germain.

Fermat's Last Theorem – A Genetic Introduction to Algebraic Number Theory, by Harold M. Edwards, 1977, Springer. A mathematical discussion of Fermat's Last Theorem, including detailed outlines of some of the early attempts at a proof.

Elementary Number Theory, by David Burton, 1980, Allyn & Bacon.

Various communications, by A. Cauchy, *C. R. Acad. Sci. Paris* **24** (1847), 407–416, 469–483.

Note au sujet de la demonstration du theoreme de Fermat, by G. Lamé, *C. R. Acad. Sci. Paris* **24** (1847), 352.

Extrait d'une lettre de M. Kummer à M. Liouville, by E.E. Kummer, *J. Math. Pures et Appl.* **12** (1847), 136. Reprinted in *Collected Papers,* Vol. I, edited by A. Weil, 1975, Springer.

4. Into Abstraction

3.1416 and All That, by P.J. Davis and W.G. Chinn. 1985, Birkhäuser. A series of stories about mathematicians and mathematics, including a chapter about Paul Wolfskehl.

The Penguin Dictionary of Curious and Interesting Numbers, by David Wells, 1986, Penguin.

The Penguin Dictionary of Curious and Interesting Puzzles, by David Wells, 1992, Penguin.

Sam Loyd and his Puzzles, by Sam Loyd (II), 1928, Barse and Co.

Mathematical Puzzles of Sam Loyd, by Sam Loyd, edited by Martin Gardner, 1959, Dover.

Riddles in Mathematics, by Eugene P. Northropp, 1944, Van Nostrand.

13 Lectures on Fermat's Last Theorem, by Paulo Ribenboim, 1980, Springer. An account of Fermat's Last Theorem, written prior to the work of Andrew Wiles, aimed at graduate students.

Mathematics: The Science of Patterns, by Keith Devlin, 1994, Scientific American Library. A beautifully illustrated book that conveys the concepts of mathematics through striking images.

Mathematics: The New Golden Age, by Keith Devlin, 1990, Penguin. A popular and detailed overview of modern mathematics, including a discussion on the axioms of mathematics.

The Concepts of Modern Mathematics, by Ian Stewart, 1995, Penguin.

Principia Mathematica, by Bertrand Russell and Alfred North Whitehead, 3 vols, 1910, 1912, 1913, Cambridge University Press.

Kurt Gödel, by G. Kreisel, Biographical Memoirs of the Fellows of the Royal Society, 1980.

A Mathematician's Apology, by G.H. Hardy, 1940, Cambridge University Press. One of the great figures of twentieth-century mathematics gives a personal account of what motivates him and other mathematicians.

Alan Turing: The Enigma of Intelligence, by Andrew Hodges, 1983, Unwin Paperbacks. An account of the life of Alan Turing, including his contribution to breaking the Enigma code.

5. Proof by Contradiction

Yutaka Taniyama and his time, by Goro Shimura, *Bulletin of the London Mathematical Society* **21** (1989), 186–196. A very personal account of the life and work of Yutaka Taniyama.

Links between stable elliptic curves and certain diophantine equations, by Gerhard Frey, *Ann. Univ. Sarav. Math. Ser.* **1** (1986), 1–40. The crucial paper that suggested a link between the Taniyama-Shimura conjecture and Fermat's Last Theorem.

6. The Secret Calculation

Genius and Biographers: the Fictionalization of Evariste Galois, by T. Rothman, *Amer. Math. Monthly* **89** (1982), 84–106. Contains a detailed list of the historical sources behind Galois's biographies, and discusses the validity of the various interpretations.

La vie d'Evariste Galois, by Paul Depuy, *Annales Scientifiques de l'Ecole Normale Supérieure* **13** (1896), 197–266.

Mes Memoirs, by Alexandre Dumas, 1967, Editions Gallimard.

Notes on Fermat's Last Theorem, by Alf van der Poorten, 1996, Wiley. A technical description of Wiles's proof aimed at mathematics undergraduates and above.

7. A Slight Problem

Modular elliptic curves and Fermat's Last Theorem, by Andrew Wiles, *Annals of Mathematics* **142** (1995), 443–551. This paper includes the bulk of Wiles's proof of the Taniyama-Shimura conjecture and Fermat's Last Theorem.

Ring-theoretic properties of certain Hecke algebras, by Richard Taylor and Andrew Wiles, *Annals of Mathematics* **142** (1995), 553–572. This paper describes the mathematics that was used to overcome the flaws in Wiles's 1993 proof.

Epilogue: Grand Unified Mathematics

An elementary introduction to the Langlands program, by Stephen Gelbart, *Bulletin of the American Mathematical Society* **10** (1984), 177–219. A technical explanation of the Langlands program aimed at mathematical researchers.

Picture Credits
. . . .

Index

· · · · · ·

Page numbers in *italic* refer to illustrations.

Abel, Niels Henrik, 3
absolute proof, 20–26, 134
absurdities, mathematical, 131, 294
Academy of Sciences, French, 109, 218
  prize for proving Fermat's Last Theorem, 111–18
ACE (Automatic Computing Engine), 156
Adleman, Leonard, 94
Adler, Alfred, 2
Agnesi, Maria, 99–100, 101, 109
Alexandria, 45–46, 50–53, 99
Alexandrian Library, 45–46, 53–54
Algarotti, Francesco, 102
algorithms, 75
amicable numbers, 58–59
Anglin, W. S., 71
Annals of Mathematics, 279
April fool E-mail, 271–73
Arago, François, 73
Arakelov, Professor S., 232
Archimedes, 45, 102
Aristotle, 54
arithmetic algebraic geometrists, 232–33
Arithmetica (Diophantus), 50–51, 54, 56, 57, 58
  Clément-Samuel Fermat's edition, 63, *64–65*
  and elliptic equations, 165
  Fermat's marginal notes, 58, 61–62, 63, 80

Latin translation, *52*, 56–57
  and Pythagorean triples, 60
axioms, 20–21, 135–36
  of arithmetic, 297
  consistency of, 139–41

Babylonians, 7, 19, 54
Bachet de Méziriac, Claude Gaspar, 56–57
  Latin translation of *Arithmetica*, *52*, 56–57
  Problèmes plaisants et delectables, 57
  weighing problem, 57, 292
Barnum, P. T., 126–27
Bell, Eric Temple, 5–6, 29, 32, 37, 105
Bernoulli family, 73–74
birthdays, shared, probability of, 42–43
Bombelli, Rafaello, 83–84
Bonaparte, Napoleon, 107, 214
Bourg-la-Reine, 212, 214, 218
Brahmagupta, 55
bridges, mathematical, 190–91
Bulletin of the London Mathematical Society, 186

calculus, 43–44
Carroll, Lewis, 126
Cauchy, Augustin Louis, 111–19, *112*, 218, 219
chessboard, mutilated, problem of, 23–25
Chevalier, Auguste, 225, 227
Chudnovsky brothers, 48
Churchill, Sir Winston Leonard Spencer, 155

cicadas, life cycles, 96–97
Circle Limit IV (Escher), *180*, 180
City of God, The (St. Augustine), 11
Clarke, Arthur C., 23
clock arithmetic, 166–69
closed groups, 228–29
Coates, John, 161, 163, *164*, 169, 189–90, 206, 209, 238, 244, 248, 262, 279–80
code breaking, 93–95, 150–56
Cohen, Paul, 143–44
Colossus (computer), 156
commutative law of addition, 135
completeness, 82–3, 136, 138, 141
complex numbers, 86, 116
computers
    early, 156–58
    unable to prove Fermat's Last Theorem, 158–61
    unable to prove Taniyama-Shimura conjecture, 211
conjectures, 67
    unifying, 282
Constantinople, 55–56
continuum hypothesis, 143–44
contradiction, proof by, 46–47, 49
Conway, Professor John H., 268
Coolidge, Julian, 37
cossists, 38
counting numbers, 11
Cretan paradox, 141
Croton, Italy, 9, 27–28
cryptography, 93–95, 150–56
cubic equations, 217
Curiosa Mathematica (Dodgson), 126
Cylon, 26–28

d'Alembert, Jean Le Rond, 87
Dalton, John, 22
Darmon, Henri, 271, 273
Deals with the Devil, 68

defective numbers, 11
    slightly, 13
Descartes, René, 39, 40, 59, 227
"Devil and Simon Flagg, The," 35, 68
d'Herbinville, Pescheux, 223, 226
Diderot, Denis, 76–77
differential geometry, 232, 234
Diffie, Whitfield, 94
Digby, Sir Kenelm, 36, 60
Diophantine problems, 51
Diophantus of Alexandria, 50, 51
    riddle of his age, 51, 291
Diophantus' Arithmetica Containing Observations by P. de Fermat, 63, *64–65*
Dirichlet, Johann Peter Gustav Lejeune, 106, 117, 168
disorder parameters, 128–30
Disquisitiones arithmeticae (Gauss), 105
Dodgson, Reverend Charles, 126
domino effect, 212
du Motel, Stéphanie-Félicie Poterine, 223, 226
Dudeney, Henry, 126
Dumas, Alexandre, 221–22

E-series, 118–19, 183–84, 190, 230–31
École Normale Supérieure, 220
École Polytechnique, 103–4, 216
economics, and calculus, 46
Eddington, Sir Arthur, 121
Egyptians, ancient, 7–8
Eichler, 175
Eiffel Tower, 109
Einstein, Albert, 17, 100
electricity, and magnetism, 184
Elements (Euclid), 46, 48, 50, 114
Elkies, Noam, 159–60, 271–72
elliptic curves, 163

elliptic equations, 163, 165–69, 181–82
  families of, 239, 243
  Frey's elliptic equation, 195–99, 202
  and modular forms, 181, 182–85, 187–94, 282
Enigma code, 150–56
Epimenides, 141
Escher, Mauritz, 180
Euclid
  infinite number of Pythagorian triples proof, 61, 292
  infinity of primes proof, 90–91
  and perfect numbers, 13
  proves that $\sqrt{2}$ is irrational, 49, 289–90
  and *reductio ad absurdum*, 46–47, 48–49
  unique factorization proof, 114
Euler, Leonhard, 32, 59, *70*
  attempts to solve Fermat's Last Theorem, 79–81, 87
  blindness and death, 87–88
  forsakes theology, 73–74
  and Königsberg bridge puzzle, 77–79
  phases of the moon algorithm, 75–76, 88
  proves existence of God, 76–77
  solves prime number theorem, 63, 66
Euler's conjecture, 159–60
Evens, Leonard, 261
Eves, Howard W., 205
excessive numbers, 11
  slightly, 13

factorization, unique, 114, 116
Faltings, Gerd, 232–34, 235, 277
Fermat, Clément-Samuel, 62–63

Fermat, Pierre de, *34*
  amateur mathematician, 37
  Arithmetica, 56, 57, 60–62
  calculus, 43–44
  career in civil service, 35–37, 56
  death, 62
  education, 35
  and elliptic equations, 165
  and Father Mersenne, 39–40
  ill with plague, 36–37
  observations and theorems, 63, 66–67
  probability theory, 40–41, 43
  reluctant to reveal proofs, 39
Fermat's Last Theorem
  challenge of, 67–69
  computers unable to prove, 158–59
  Fermat's proof, 283–84
  Miyaoka's 'proof', 232–35
  partial proofs
    by computer, 158
    Germain's method, 104–6
    $n=3$ (Euler), 81, 86, 89–90
    $n=4$ (Fermat), 80–81, 89–90
    $n=5$ (Dirichlet and Legendre), 106
    $n=7$ (Lamé), 106
    $n=$irregular prime (Kummer and Mirimanoff), 157–58
  publication of, 62–63
  and Pythagoras's equation, 29–32, 60–62
  skepticism as to existence of proof, 117–118
  simplicity of statement, 6, 68
  and Taniyama-Shimura conjecture, 196–99, 201, 244, 245
  and undecidability, 143–44, 147
  why called 'Last', 67
  Wiles's proof *see* Wiles, Andrew

Fermatean triple, 61
Flach, Matheus, 238
four-dimensional shapes, 233–34
four-dimensional space, 179–81
Fourier, Jean Baptiste Joseph, 219
"14–15" puzzle, 127–31, 199
fractions, 11, 49, 81–82
Frey, Gerhard, 195–99, 202
Frey's elliptic equation, 195–99, 201–2
friendly numbers, 58–59
fundamental particles of matter, 22–23
fundamental theorem of arithmetic, 114
fundamental truths, 134–35
Furtwängler, Professor P., 138–39

Galileo Galilei, 37
Galois, Évariste, 3, *213*
  birth, 212
  duel with d'Herbinville, 223, 225–26
  education, 214–16, 220
  final notes, 223, *224*, 225–26, 227
  funeral, 226
  and group theory, 228–29, 230–31
  and quintic equations, 218, 219–20, 225, 227–28
  revolutionary career, 218–22
game theory, 147–48, 297
Gardner, Martin, 58, 133
Gauss, Carl Friedrich, 105, 107–9, 160
geometry, 7–8
Gerbert of Aurillac, 55
Germain, Sophie, 97, *98*, 101–5
  career as a physicist, 108–9

  and Évariste Galois, 221
  relationship with Gauss, 107–8, 109
  strategy for Fermat's Last Theorem, 104–6
Gibbon, Edward, 99
Globe, Le, 219
Gödel, Kurt, 133, 138–39, *140*, 141
  undecidable statements, 142–43
Goldbach, Christian, 81
Gombaud, Antoine, 40–41
Gouvea, Fernando, 279
Government Code and Cypher School, 150–55
gravity, theories of, 22
group theory, 228–29
Guardian, 250

hammers, harmony of, 15
Hardy, G. H., 1, 2–4, 47, 146, 147, 160–61, 171
Hecke algebras, 276–77
Hein, Piet, 255
Heisenberg, Werner, 142–43
Hellman, Martin, 94
Hermite, Charles, 3
hieroglyphics, 191
Hilbert, David, 92–94, 133, 136, *137*, 138
  and basic axioms, 135–36
  and Fermat's Last Theorem, 206–7
  23 problems, 136, 144
Hilbert's Hotel, 92–93
Hippasus, 50
History of Mathematics (Montucla) 102
Hypatia, 99, 101
hyperbolic space, 179–81
Iamblichus, 14–15

Illusie, Luc, 256, 259
imaginary numbers, 81, 84–87, 114–15
induction, proof by, 211–12, 297–99
infinite descent, method of, 80–81
infinity, 55, 91–93, 158–59
International Congress of Mathematicians
  Berkeley (1986), 199
  Paris (1900), 136
intuition, and probability, 41
invariants, 130, 131, 199
Inventiones Mathematicae, 255
irrational numbers, 47, 49, 81–82
Iwasawa theory, 237, 238, 274, 275

Journal de Mathématique pures et appliquées, 227

Kanada, Yasumasa, 48
Katz, Nick, *240*, 241–43, 256–58, 259
knot invariants, 130–31, 221
Kolyvagin-Flach method, 237–38, 241–43, 257–58, 259, 269, 274–75
Königliche Gesellschaft der Wissenschaften, 123–25, 255
Königsberg bridge puzzle, 77–79
Kovalevsky, Sonya, 101
Kronecker, Leopold, 47–48
Kummer, Ernst Eduard, 113–14, *115*, 116–19

L-series, 168
Lagrange, Joseph-Louis, 87, 104, 219
Lamé, Gabriel, 106, *110*, 111, 113–14, 116–19

Landau, Edmund, 100, 132
Langlands, Robert, 192–93, 282–283
Langlands program, 192–93, 232, 282–83
Last Problem, The (Bell), 5–6, 29, 32, 68
Le Blanc, Antoine-August, 104
  see also Germain, Sophie
Legendre, Adrien-Marie, 106
Leibniz, Gottfried, 84
liar's paradox, 141–42
Libri-Carrucci dalla Sommaja, Count Guglielmo, 103, 221
limericks, 279, 283
Liouville, Joseph, 113, 227–28
Lipman, Joseph, 261
Littlewood, John Edensor, 160–61
logic, mathematical, 134–35
logicians, 134–35, 143
loopiness, in rivers, 17–18
Loyd Sam, 126–31
Loyd's puzzle *see* "14–15" puzzle
lyre, tuning strings on, 14–16

M-series, 181–85, 190, 230–31
magnetism, and electricity, 184
Mathematical Magic Show (Gardner), 58
mathematical proof, 20–21, 23–26
Mathematician's Apology, A (Hardy), 2–3, 47, 146
mathematicians
  collaboration amongst, 4–5
  and compulsion of curiosity 145–47
  in India and Arabia, 54–56
  mathematical life, 2–4
  require absolute proof, 134–36, 138

mathematicians *continued*
  secretive nature,   38–39
  self-doubt of,   72–73
  youthfulness,   2–3
mathematics
  foundation for science,   26
  objective subject,   27–28
  relationship with science,   17, 18
  in seventeenth century,   37–38
Mathematics of Great Amateurs
  (Coolidge),   37
Mathematische Annalen,   171
Mazur, Barry,   190–91, 199, 201,
  243, 244–45, 248, 255
Mersenne, Father Marin,   38–39
Method, The (Heiberg),   45
Milo,   9, 27
Mirimanoff, Dimitri,   158
Miyaoka, Yoichi,   232–35
Miyaoka inequality,   234
modular forms,   175, 179–82
  and elliptic equations,   181,
    183–85, 188–94, 282
Monde, Le,   250–51
Montucla, Jean-Étienne,   102
moon, predicting phases of,   75–
  76
Moore, Professor L. T.,   44
Mozans, H. J.,   109
musical harmony, principles of 14–
  16

natural numbers,   81–82
negative numbers,   81–84
New York, subway graffiti,   235
New York Times,   232, 251, 252, 260,
  279
Newton, Isaac,   44, 74, 75
Noether, Emmy,   100–101
nothingness, concept of,   54–55
number line,   83–85, 166–67

numbers, relationships between   11
numerals, Indo-Arab,   54–55
Oberwolfach symposium (1984)
  194–99
Olbers, Heinrich,   105
order and chaos,   17
overestimated prime conjecture
  160

Paganini, Nicolò,   59
parallelism, philosophy of,   232,
  235
parasites, life cycles,   96–97
particle physics,   22–23
Pascal, Blaise,   38, 40–41, 43–44
Penrose, Roger,   178
Penrose tilings,   178–79
People,   251, 268
perfect numbers,   11–13
philosopher, word coined by
  Pythagoras,   9–10
pi (π),   17–18
Pillow Problems (Dodgson),   126
Pinch, Richard,   262–63
Plato,   99
Porges, Arthur,   35, 68
points (dice game),   41
polynomials,   217–18
prime numbers,   63, 66
  and Fermat's Last Theorem,
    89–91
  Germain primes,   105–6
  infinity of,   90–93
  irregular primes,   116–17, 158
  practical applications,   93–97
  333,333,331 not prime,   159
probability,   40–44
  counterintuitive,   42–43
Problèmes plaisants et delectables
  (Bachet),   57
puzzles, compendiums of,   126

Pythagoras
  abhors irrational numbers,   47,
    49–50
  at Croton,   9–10, 27–28
  death,   28
  and mathematical proof,   25–
    26
  and musical harmony,   14–16
  and perfect numbers,   11–13
  and study of numbers,   7
  travels,   7–8
Pythagoras's equation,   27–29
  "cubed" version,   30–32
  and Fermat's Last Theorem 32,
    60–62
  whole number solutions,   28–
    30
Pythagoras's theorem,   6–7, 19–
  20, 25–26, 287–88
Pythagorean Brotherhood,   9–11,
  13, 26–28, 46, 47, 98
Pythagorean triples,   26–29, 60,
  292

quadratic equations,   216–17
quantum physics,   142–43
quartic equations,   217–18
quintic equations,   217–18, 219,
  225, 227–29

Ramanujan, Srinivasa,   2–3
rational numbers,   10–11
rearrangement of equations 195–
  96
recipes, mathematical,   7–8, 218
reductio ad absurdum,   46–47, 49–
  50
reflectional symmetry,   176
Reidemeister, Kurt,   130
religion, and probability,   43
Ribenboim, Paulo,   133

Ribet, Ken,   199, *200*, 201–3, 245,
  248–49, *254*, 266–67, 282
  Fermat Information Service,   260
  and significance of Taniyama-
    Shimura conjecture,   199,
    201–3
river ratio,   17–18
Rivest, Ronald,   94
Rosetta stone,   191
rotational symmetry,   176–77
Rubin, Professor Karl,   246–47,
  276–77
Russell, Bertrand,   21, 41, 133

St. Augustine (of Hippo),   11
*Sam Loyd and his Puzzles: An Auto-
  biographical Review*,   126–27
Samos, Greece,   8–9
Sarnak, Peter,   263, 269
Schlichting, Dr. F.,   133, 294–95
scientific proof,   21–22
scientific theories,   22–23
scrambling and unscrambling messages,   93–95, 148, 150–56
Selmer groups,   264
Shamir, Adi,   94
Shimura, Goro,   171, *172*, 173–75,
  179, 182, 183
  relationship with Taniyama,
    185–87, 188
  and Taniyama-Shimura conjec-
    ture,   187–90, 251
Shimura-Taniyama conjecture *see*
  Taniyama-Shimura conjecture
Silverman, Bob,   262
Isaac Newton Institute, Cambridge,
  4–5, 244
*Sir Isaac Newton's Philosophy Explain'd
  for the Use of Ladies* (Algarotti),
  102
6, perfection of,   11–12

Skewes, S.,   160–61
Skewes's number,   160–61
sociable numbers,   59–60
Socrates,   110
Somerville, Mary,   103
square, symmetries of,   176–77
square-cube sandwiches,   59
square root of one,   83–84
square root of two,   48–49, 82–83,
    288–90
strings
  and particles,   23
  vibrating,   14–15, 16, 17
Suzuki, Misako,   186–87
symmetry,   175–82

Taniyama, Yutaka,   *170,* 171, 173–
    75, 179, 182
  death,   185–87
  influence of,   188
  and Taniyama-Shimura conjec-
    ture,   182–85
Taniyama-Shimura conjecture,
    184–85, 187–94
  and Fermat's Last Theorem 194–
    99, 201–3
  Wiles and,   194, 203, 205–12,
    236–39, 241–43, 251, 280–81
Taniyama-Weil conjecture *see*
    Taniyama-Shimura conjecture
Taylor, Richard,   262, 269, *270,*
    273, 276–77
Thales,   26
Theano,   9, 97–98
theorems,   66–67
*Theory of Games and Economic
    Behaviour, The* (von Neumann),
    147
Thomson, J. J.,   22
three-body problem,   75
tiled surfaces, symmetry of,   177–79

Titchmarsh, E. C.,   147
Tokyo, international symposium
    (1955),   182
translational symmetry,   176–77
trichotomy, law of,   134–35
truels,   148, 297
Turing, Alan Mathison,   148–57

uncertainty principle,   142–43
undecidability theorems,   139,
    141–44

von Neumann, John,   139, 147–48

Wagstaff, Samuel S.,   158
Wallis, John,   36, 40, 60
weighing problem,   57, 292
Weil, André,   141, 189
Weil conjecture *see* Taniyama-
    Shimura conjecture
Weyl, Hermann,   136
whole numbers,   11
Wiener Kreis (Viennese Circle),   139
Wiles, Andrew,   *xx, 162, 204, 254,
    278*
  adolescence and Fermat's Last
    Theorem,   5–6, 32, 71–72
  graduate student days,   161, 163
  tackles elliptic equations,   163,
    165–66, 169
  and Taniyama-Shimura conjec-
    ture,   194, 203, 205–12, 236–
    39, 241–43, 251, 280–82
  uses Galois's groups,   229–31,
    236, 273
  announces proof of Fermat's Last
    Theorem,   1–2, 5, 33, 244–47,
    250
  reaction of media,   250–53
  mathematical celebrity,   251–53,
    268

submits proof for verification
    255–58
proof flawed,   257–68, 269,
    272–73
proof revised,   273–77
proof published,   279–83
wins Wolf Prize,   305
collects Wolfskehl Prize,   331
and the future,   331

Wiles, Nada,   210, 243, 259, 275–
    76
Wolf Prize,   283
Wolfskehl, Paul,   *120*, 121–23
Wolfskehl Prize,   123–25, 131–33,
    284

Zagier, Don,   232
zero, function of,   54–55